Bring Science Alive!
Space

TCi™

NEXT GENERATION SCIENCE STANDARDS For States, By States

*NGSS is a registered trademark of Achieve. Neither Achieve nor the lead states and partners that developed the Next Generation Science Standards were involved in the production of this product, and do not endorse it.

Co-Chief Executive Officer
Bert Bower

Co-Chief Executive Officer
Amy Larson

Chief Operating Officer
Ellen Hardy

Director of Product Development
Maria Favata

Strategic Product Manager
Nathan Wellborne

Managing Editor
Ariel Stein

Senior Science Editor
Rebecca Ou

Senior Strategic Editor
Kim Merlino

***Space* Lead Editor**
Rebecca Ou

Science Content Developers
Karin Akre
Tanya Dewey
Mantissa Johnston
Suzanne Lyons
Abigail Pillitteri
Clay Walton
Jennifer Yeh

Editors
Helene Engler
Sally Isaacs
Lauren Kent
Marlene Martzke
Tylar Pendgraft
Alex White
Ginger Wu

Writers
Sarah Martin
Linda Blumenthal
Sabre Duren
Katie Ewing
Rebecca Mikulec
Laura Prescott
Molly Wetterschneider

Illustrator/Graphic Artists
Andrew Dakhil
Martha Iserman
Aki Ruiz

Production and Design
Jodi Forrest
Jen Valenzuela
Michelle Vella

Web and Print Designer
Sarah Osentowski

Video Developer
Dominic Mercurio

Director of Operations
Marsha Ifurung

Investigation UX Testing
Davin Kunovsky

Software
Morris Thai
Christopher Ching
Robert Julius
Gabriel Redig

Software Quality Assurance
Mrudula Sarode

Art Direction
Julia Foug

Teachers' Curriculum Institute
PO Box 1327
Rancho Cordova, CA 95741

Customer Service: 800-497-6138
www.teachtci.com

ISBN 978-1-58371-073-9
3 4 5 6 7 8 9 10 -WC- 23 22 21 20 19

Manufactured by Webcrafters, Inc., Madison, WI
United States of America, June 2019, Job # WC1903503

Welcome to *Bring Science Alive!*

Welcome to *Bring Science Alive! Space.* We've created this program to help you understand the science and engineering ideas in the Next Generation Science Standards (NGSS). Now I'm sure you are super busy and have a lot on your mind each day. So why should you care about the vastness of space and the celestial bodies in it? Or the long list of science standards created by adults who are really into science?

While you may not be thinking about space, or NGSS, every day, we at TCI are. The TCI teachers who created this program thought long and hard about how to make space exciting and understandable. So, you'll find very straightforward text, gorgeous photos, and super-helpful illustrations. Most importantly, we created a series of investigations that will engage and delight you. You'll travel the solar system and turn your classroom into a planetarium to understand the motions of planets, moons, and stars.

What does this all mean for you? I promise, if you're anything like the students I've taught using this curriculum, you'll never look up at the moon or the stars in the same way again.

This program is going to make you an instant expert on space. You'll soon be explaining to your family and friends why the moon seems to change shape, what causes a solar eclipse, and why there are seasons. And every time you look up into space, you will feel the pride and satisfaction that comes from knowing what was previously unknown.

Enjoy the program!

Bert Bower
TCI CEO and Founder

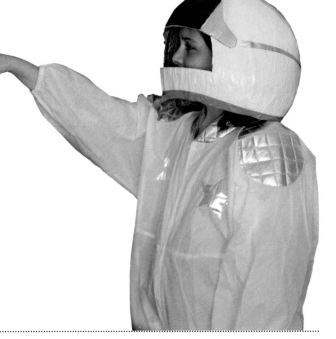

Science Content Scholars

David Begun, Ph.D.
Professor, Population Biology and
Evolution and Ecology
University of California, Davis

Gillian Bowser, Ph.D.
Research Scientist, Natural Resource
Ecology Laboratory
Colorado State University

John Czworkowski, Ph.D.
Chemistry Instructor
Grossmont College
El Cajon, California

Tanya Dewey, Ph.D.
Research Scientist, Biology
Department
Colorado State University

Brian W. Holmes, Ph.D.
Professor, Physics and Astronomy
San José State University
San José, California

Ehsan Khatami, Ph.D.
Assistant Professor, Physics and
Astronomy
San José State University
San José, California

Charles Liu, Ph.D.
Professor, Astrophysics
The College of Staten Island
City University of New York

Michael J. Passow, Ed.D.
Adjunct Associate Research Scientist,
Lamont-Doherty Earth Observatory
Columbia University

Lesilee Rose, Ph.D.
Professor, Department of Molecular
and Cellular Biology
College of Biological Sciences
University of California, Davis

Paul Ruscher, Ph.D.
Dean, Science Division
Lane Community College
Eugene, Oregon
Fellow, *American Meteorological
Society*

Science Teacher Consultants

Kenneth Amunrud
Science Teacher
Joseph George Middle School
*Alum Rock Union Elementary School
District*
San José, California

Nancy Anderson
Middle School Science Teacher
Mannington Township School
Mannington Township, New Jersey

Amy Argento
Science Teacher
Jefferson Middle School
Torrance Unified School District
Torrance, California

Noel Berghout
Math and Science Teacher
Jane Lathrop Stanford Middle School
Palo Alto Unified School District
Palo Alto, California

Carla Dalfonso
Science Specialist
Joe Serna Jr. Charter School
Lodi Unified School District
Lodi, California

Nora Haddad
Science Teacher
*San Martin/Gwinn Environmental
Science Academy*
Morgan Hill Unified School District
Santa Clara County, California

Marsenne Kendall
Chemistry Teacher
Half Moon Bay High School
Cabrillo Unified School District
Half Moon Bay, California

Ann M. Lorey
Science Department Supervisor and
Instructional Coach
Jane Lathrop Stanford Middle School
Palo Alto Unified School District
Palo Alto, California

Kevin Lynch
Science Teacher
J.L. Stanford Middle School
Palo Alto Unified School District
Palo Alto, California

Michael Passow
Earth Science Teacher (ret.)
White Plains Middle School
White Plains, New York

Stephanie Ruzicka
Science Teacher
Horner Junior High School
Fremont Unified School District
Fremont, California

Michelle Serrano
Secondary Science Curriculum
Specialist
Hemet Unified School District
Hemet, California

Mathematics Teacher Consultant

Kenneth Amunrud
Mathematics Teacher
Joseph George Middle School
*Alum Rock Union Elementary
School District*
San José, California

Reading Consultant

Marilyn Chambliss, Ph.D.
Associate Professor of Education
Emerita
University of Maryland

How to Read the Table of Contents

The table of contents is your guide to *Bring Science Alive! Space*. In addition to showing the parts of your Student Text, it shows the exciting science and engineering investigations you will be doing in class.

CONTENTS

Each unit has a fun and interesting phenomenon or problem that will give you a focus for learning.

Unit 1

The Earth-Sun-Moon System 2

Phenomenon-Based Storyline Many adults have misconceptions about Earth's movement in space. How can you use models to help them understand these patterns?

Investigations integrate:

- science and engineering practices,
- crosscutting concepts,
- and disciplinary core ideas.

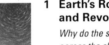

Investigations Build and use your classroom planetarium to develop a model that explains patterns caused by Earth's rotation and revolution.

Reading Further features are fun, interesting articles that promote literacy and help you engage with the lesson content in more depth.

The lesson title identifies the science topic.

An essential question prepares you for inquiry—and for using evidence to explain how the natural world works.

Investigations Use your classroom planetarium to develop a model that explains how Earth's tilted axis is involved in causing seasonal patterns.

Engineering Design will help prepare you for success in solving engineering-focused investigations. Look for the symbol with three circles to see how engineering design is integrated into the lessons.

Investigations Use your classroom planetarium to develop a model that explains the causes of moon phases.

Investigations Use your classroom planetarium to develop a model that explains how the orientation of Earth, the sun, and the moon cause eclipses.

Key Science Concepts are large, memorable visual representations of the most important ideas of the lesson.

Performance Assessment
Use what you learned about the Earth-sun-moon system to develop a model and use it to create a film that educates adults on a pattern that can be observed from Earth.

A Performance Assessment related to the unit's storyline inspires you to use science and engineering practices, crosscutting concepts, and disciplinary core ideas.

CONTENTS

The Design of the Program

Unit 1

The Earth-Sun-Moon System

Phenomenon-Based Storyline Many adults have misconceptions about Earth's movement in space. How can you use models to help them understand these patterns?

Why do the stars and sun appear and move across the sky?

Key Science Concept:
Patterns of the Sun and Stars Due to Earth's Rotation and Revolution

 Engineering Design:
Solving the Problem of Locating Stars

Investigations Build and use your classroom planetarium to develop a model that explains patterns caused by Earth's rotation and revolution.

Performance Assessment
Use what you learned about the Earth-sun-moon system to develop a model and use it to create a film that educates adults on a pattern that can be observed from Earth.

 Engineering Design will help prepare you for success in solving engineering-focused investigations. Look for this symbol to see how engineering design is integrated into the lesson.

Unit 2

The Solar System 68

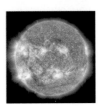

Unit 3

The Solar System and Beyond........................128

Phenomenon-Based Storyline You are a science consultant meeting with the director of a new space movie. Your role is to help ensure the movie is scientifically accurate as well as entertaining.

Investigations Use models to correct misconceptions about how the solar system formed.

Investigations Use scale models to describe and compare distances between objects in the solar system and within the universe.

Engineering Challenge Develop multiple damping devices to protect a camera as it travels into space. Then test a design to identify points of failure and make improvements.

Performance Assessment Using your knowledge, come up with and pitch a climax scene for a movie involving gravity. Utilizing a model, you will demonstrate how the scene is scientifically accurate while remaining entertaining.

Key Science Concepts

Figures

Interdisciplinary Science makes the connections between the life, earth, and physical sciences.

Interdisciplinary Science

Primary Sources

Bring Science Alive! Programs

Bring Science Alive! is a collection of nine middle school science programs that are 100 percent aligned to NGSS. These programs can be organized into three year-long courses for either integrated-science or discipline-specific learning progressions. Programs are well coordinated to crosscutting concepts such as patterns, energy and matter, and structure and function. Science and engineering practices are integrated with disciplinary core ideas and crosscutting concepts in engaging and challenging investigations.

Weather and Climate

Investigate the atmosphere and energy transfer, the water cycle, air pressure and air masses, weather prediction, climate factors and patterns, and Earth's changing climate.

Planet Earth

Construct explanations about Earth's natural resources, the rock and water cycles, rock layers, fossils, geologic time, plate tectonics, and natural hazards using varied time scales.

Space

Model cause and effect relationships involving Earth's rotation, revolution, and tilted axis; lunar phases and eclipses, the solar system, galaxies, and the universe.

Bring Science Alive! integrates Science and Engineering Practices, Crosscutting Concepts, and Disciplinary Core Ideas to result in Three Dimensional Learning.

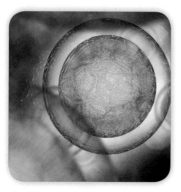

Cells and Genetics

Use evidence to explore traits, survival, and reproduction; the structure and functions of body systems and cells; genes and inheritance of traits, mutations, and engineering and genetics.

Ecosystems

Model interdependency in ecosystems, photosynthesis and cellular respiration, energy flow and cycling of matter, biodiversity, and explore the human impacts on ecosystems and biodiversity.

Adaptations

Identify cause and effect relationships between Earth's history and the fossil record, natural selection and changes in species, genes and patterns of inheritance; and humans, evolution, and heredity.

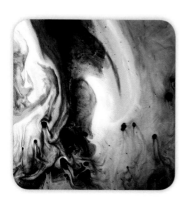

Matter

Apply the concepts of conservation of matter and energy transfer to model atoms, molecules, particle motion, state changes, and chemical reactions; and explore engineering solutions involving chemical reactions.

Forces and Energy

Solve engineering problems and plan investigations about forces, Newton's Laws of Motion; kinetic and potential energy; thermal energy, heat, and the thermal properties of matter.

Waves

Explore mechanical waves and their properties by looking at patterns in data, waves in different mediums, the wave model of light, properties of light waves, and technologies using waves to transfer information.

How to Use this Program

The components of *Bring Science Alive!* provide the tools needed for a complete learning system that integrates science and engineering practices, crosscutting concepts, and disciplinary core ideas. Designed for deep learning, *Bring Science Alive!* lessons use research-based learning strategies to reach all students.

1 Each new lesson begins with a **Lesson Presentation** preview activity that teachers access through their online subscriptions. Lesson presentations are the interactive guides at the heart of every TCI lesson.

2 Guided by the Lesson Presentation and using the **Science Materials Kits** and their **Interactive Student Notebooks**, students conduct one or more investigations that powerfully integrate the three dimensions of NGSS. While investigating, students build understandings that they will need in order to complete the end-of-unit performance assessment.

4

The lesson concludes with students demonstrating their mastery of the science and engineering practices, crosscutting concepts, and disciplinary core ideas through a variety of paper and online **assessment tools**.

3

In their online student subscriptions, students expand their understanding by engaging with their dynamic **Student Text** and working through an **Interactive Tutorial**. Then they process what they have learned in their online **Interactive Student Notebook**.

Alternatively, students can read from the hardcover Student Edition and process their learning in a consumable Interactive Student Notebook.

Next Generation Science Standards for Three Dimensional Learning

The Next Generation Science Standards (NGSS) were written to change the way science is taught in K–12 classrooms and reflect recent advances in science, technology, and the understanding of how students learn. NGSS aims to help students prepare for college, 21st-century careers, scientific literacy needed as citizens, and competition in an increasingly global economy.

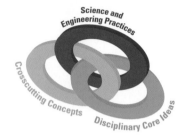

Performance Expectations

NGSS standards are called *performance expectations* and are worded to explain what students should be able to do in assessments at the completion of a unit of study. The performance expectations are built on the foundation provided by *A Framework for K-12 Science Education* (2012). Every performance expectation integrates the three dimensions described in the Framework: science and engineering practices, crosscutting concepts, and disciplinary core ideas. Also included in the performance expectations are clarification statements providing examples and other details, and assessment boundaries to guide test development. The graphic shows an example of how all the pieces result in a coherent standard to guide instruction.

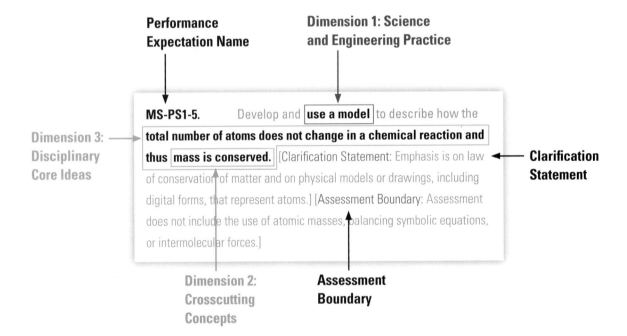

Dimension 1: Science and Engineering Practices

Science and Engineering Practices, such as developing and using models, describe what actual scientists and engineers do. Students develop the ability to use these practices through investigating the natural and designed worlds. While engaged in practices, students develop understandings described by the disciplinary core ideas and crosscutting concepts. The eight practices involve ways of thinking about investigations and engineering problems, the integration of mathematics, and social interactions. Without any particular order implied, these eight practices help define what has been called "scientific inquiry" and "engineering processes."

Bring Science Alive! investigations guide students to develop and reflect on their use of science and engineering practices.

Dimension 2: Crosscutting Concepts

Crosscutting Concepts, such as patterns and cause and effect, are the themes that organize students' understanding of science and engineering in the same way that scientists and engineers do. They can also be thought of as lenses all students should use as they explore and describe phenomena related to physical, earth and space, and life sciences. These "big picture" concepts are important in helping students make connections across all disciplines of science and engineering.

Each lesson focuses on a crosscutting concept that is explained in the lesson introduction and developed through the lesson.

Dimension 3: Disciplinary Core Ideas

Disciplinary Core Ideas are focused statements of content specific to the physical, earth and space, life sciences, or engineering. There are a limited number of core ideas, avoiding "mile wide, inch deep" curricula. The purpose of limiting the number of science concepts is to allow students the time they need for learning science and engineering practices through investigations. NGSS core ideas assume that students have mastered the content of previous grades and are ready for more advanced learning.

Students learn disciplinary core ideas by collecting evidence and building arguments through investigations, research, reading, and using multimedia tools.

Science and Engineering Practices | Dimension 1

The Next Generation Science Standards (NGSS) emphasize learning by investigating the natural world through the practices of scientific inquiry. Being able to use science understandings and practices allows students to investigate further questions about the natural world and solve meaningful engineering problems. NGSS identifies eight practices of science and engineering. Each lesson of *Bring Science Alive!* provides scaffolded instruction and reflection of one or more of these practices.

Asking Questions and Defining Problems

Science often begins by asking meaningful questions that can be answered by explanations supported by evidence. Similarly, engineering may begin with a question but always involves defining a problem that can be solved by carefully-tested solutions. Students learn to ask supporting questions that clarify and move them forward in investigations and solving engineering problems.

Developing and Using Models

Science and engineering use models to represent very large, very small, or very complicated systems. Using models helps scientists and engineers develop questions and explanations, gather data and make predictions, and communicate ideas to others. Students learn to develop, interpret, and modify models to describe scientific phenomena and test their engineering solutions.

Planning and Carrying Out Investigations

Scientific investigations are planned and carried out to describe a phenomena, test a hypothesis, or model how the world works. They are also used to test engineering solutions. Students design investigations that generate data for evidence to support their claims and learn how to be systematic in their methods so that they can obtain the most precise results.

Analyzing and Interpreting Data

All the data in the world is meaningless unless it can be presented in a form that reveals patterns and relationships and allows results to be communicated. Students analyze and interpret data by organizing their data into tables and graphs to identify overall trends and specific patterns.

Using Mathematics and Computational Thinking

Scientists and engineers use mathematics to represent physical variables and their relationships and to make quantitative descriptions and predictions. Students use mathematics aligned to the Common Core State Standards to analyze data for patterns and answer scientific questions. They also use mathematics to test and compare scientific arguments and engineering solutions.

Constructing Explanations and Designing Solutions

The goal of scientific inquiry is to construct explanations for why things happen. Likewise, the goal of engineering is to design solutions to people's problems. Students engage in constructing explanations when they make sense of the data they collect during investigations and when they propose solutions to engineering problems.

Engaging in Argument from Evidence

Argument is a process for comparing different explanations and solutions, and determining which is best. Reasoning and argument based on evidence are important for identifying the best explanation or the best solution to a design problem. Students engage in critical discussions to practice listening to, comparing, and evaluating competing explanations and solutions.

Obtaining, Evaluating, and Communicating Information

Researching, reading, interpreting, and producing scientific and technical text is an important part of science and engineering. Students learn to recognize key ideas, identify bias, distinguish observations from inferences, arguments from explanations, and claims from evidence. They communicate their findings orally, in writing, and through extended discussions.

The Next Generation Science Standards (NGSS) underscore the importance of making connections between the life, earth, physical sciences, and engineering. The seven crosscutting concepts are designed to do just this. While the seven overarching concepts are the same from kindergarten through twelfth grade, the details increase in complexity as students progress. *Bring Science Alive!* develops crosscutting concepts in conjunction with appropriate disciplinary core ideas and science and engineering practices throughout the Student Text, Lesson Presentation activities and investigations, and assessments.

Patterns

Middle school students relate macroscopic patterns to microscopic structures, identify relationships that show patterns in rates of change, analyze numerical data on graphs and charts for patterns, and identify patterns that lead to understanding cause-and-effect relationships.

Cause and Effect

Through investigations and discussion, students come to appreciate that a phenomenon may have more than one cause, that the likelihood of certain types of outcomes must be expressed in terms of probability, and that by recognizing cause-and-effect relationships they can make predictions in science and engineering. They also discover how relationships can be causal or correlational but that not all correlational relationships are causal.

Scale, Proportion, and Quantity

Phenomena involving time, space, or energy can be observed at different scales. The function of a system may change, depending on the scale at which it is observed. Students learn that some natural systems are either too large or too small to be directly observed, but they can explored using models of various scales. Mathematical reasoning becomes increasingly important to understanding and communicating scientific ideas as students learn that certain relationships can be represented as expressions or equations and that proportional relationships are useful for describing relationships between many scientific quantities.

Systems and System Models

The concept of a system as an organized group of parts is essential in all science disciplines and, certainly, for designing, building, and testing solutions to engineering problems. Throughout their investigations, students use the concept of systems to show how parts interact both within and outside a system, as well as how systems have sub-systems. Models are essential for understanding inputs and outputs and that energy and matter flow through many systems.

Energy and Matter

Energy and matter flow into, out of, and within both natural systems and designed systems. Students learn to track energy flow through both natural and designed systems. They use that understanding to describe the role energy plays in cycling of matter, and in describing the many forms energy takes as it is transferred from one part of a system to another.

Structure and Function

This crosscutting concept is closely related to systems and system models. Students learn to analyze the functions of all parts of a system by examining their shapes, properties, and their relationships to each other. Designing and building structures for particular functions also requires consideration of the parts' shapes and the materials from which they are made.

Stability and Change

Like structure and function, stability and change is a concept that directly supports the understanding of systems. Students' explanations of stability and change in systems include how changes to one part affect other parts of the system, how change can be gradual or sudden, and how equilibrium is maintained through feedback mechanisms.

Disciplinary Core Ideas

The Next Generation Science Standards include a limited number of compelling scientific and engineering ideas to ensure that K–12 students learn and engage in the practices of science and engineering. Every *Bring Science Alive!* lesson allows students to build understanding of the disciplinary core ideas through the uses of these practices and the crosscutting concepts.

Core Idea ESS1: Earth's Place in the Universe

Planet Earth is part of a vast universe that has developed over a huge expanse of time and can be understood using observation, physics, and chemistry. Middle school students learn how gravitational forces hold the solar system together; explain patterns that result in lunar phases, eclipses, and seasons; and explore Earth's history by understanding rock strata and the fossil record.

Core Idea ESS2: Earth's Systems

Earth is made up of a set of dynamic systems whose interactions and processes determine how Earth changes over time. Students study the effects of energy flows and the cycling of matter in many of these systems, such as plate tectonics, the water cycle, weather systems, and changes due to weathering and erosion.

Core Idea ESS3: Earth and Human Activity

Humans depend on, are affected by, and cause changes to Earth's systems. Students learn how many natural resources are limited in quantity or distribution, the causes of natural hazards and likelihood that they will occur, and how humans impact the biosphere and can design solutions to lessen their impacts.

Core Idea LS1: From Molecules to Organisms: Structures and Processes

The functioning of all organisms is closely related to the structures that make them up, on scales ranging from individual molecules to whole body systems. Middle school students study structures such as cells, tissue, organs, and organ systems; and functions like behaviors, photosynthesis, cellular respiration, and sensory responses.

Core Idea LS2: Ecosystems: Interactions, Energy, and Dynamics

Ecosystems are dynamic systems in which organisms interact with one another and nonliving resources. They can be described by the flow of energy and cycling of matter. Students study patterns of interdependency; producers, consumers, and decomposers; and the effects of disruptions to ecosystems.

Core Idea LS3: Heredity: Inheritance and Variation of Traits

Heredity is the mechanism by which traits are passed via genes from parents to offspring. Middle school students learn that

genes control the production of proteins that affect traits, how sexual reproduction results in variation in inherited genetic information, and about the effects of mutations on traits.

Core Idea LS4: Biological Evolution: Unity and Diversity

Biological evolution explains both the similarities and differences among species and their history on Earth. Students learn how the fossil record and embryological development indicate that species are related, how natural and artificial selection result in changes to species over time, and how changes in biodiversity can affect humans.

Core Idea PS1: Matter and Its Interactions

The existence of atoms is fundamental to understanding the characteristics and behavior of matter. Middle school students apply the concepts of atoms and molecules to explain the existence of different substances, properties of matter, changes in state, and conservation of matter in chemical reactions.

Core Idea PS2: Motion and Stability: Forces and Interactions

Forces are a tool for describing the interactions between objects and for explaining and predicting the effects of those interactions. In middle school, students begin to quantitatively describe the effects of forces and learn to describe forces that act at a distance using fields.

Core Idea PS3: Energy

Energy is a tool for explaining and predicting interactions between objects. In middle school, students learn that systems often involve kinetic and potential energy. Energy concepts are extended to explain more complex interactions, such as those involved in chemical reactions, living things, and Earth systems.

Core Idea PS4: Waves and Their Applications in Technologies for Information Transfer

Waves are repeating patterns of motion that transfer energy from place to place without overall displacement of matter. Students use properties, such as wavelength, frequency, and amplitude, to understand the behaviors of wave-like phenomena, including light, sound, and water waves. Scientists and engineers also use wave properties to encode information as digitized signals for communication.

Core Idea ETS1: Engineering Design

Engineers solve problems using a design process involving specific practices and knowledge. Students in the middle grades learn the importance of defining criteria and constraints with precision, testing solutions, and using test results to improve solutions iteratively to achieve optimal designs.

Integrating Engineering with Science Learning

The Next Generation Science Standards describe engineering as a process similar to, and just as important as, scientific inquiry. The four engineering design performance expectations for middle school require students to understand how to define criteria and constraints, evaluate competing design solutions, analyze data to combine several designs, and develop models to test and refine proposed designs.

Student Text

In *Bring Science Alive!* student texts, engineering design is well integrated with the scientific core ideas of the lesson, including all the same support as other parts of the lesson: interactive tutorials, vocabulary development, and assessments.

Engineering design sections are identified by the symbol with three circles.

Engineering vocabulary is developed in the same ways as science vocabulary.

Look for this Engineering Design symbol throughout *Bring Science Alive!*

Engineering Design

Investigations

In *Bring Science Alive!'s* engineering challenges, students use science and engineering practices to solve fun, interesting problems that have the potential to help answer scientific questions, improve lives, protect the environment, entertain, and delight.

The consistent engineering design process in *Bring Science Alive!'s* engineering challenges provides a clear road map for approaching design problems. Using it, students will decide when to define the problem, develop possible solutions, and optimize their designs.

Each engineering challenge focuses on one or two easy-to-learn engineering skills. By the time they complete the program, students will have a full set of tools for tackling any design problem.

English Language Arts & Literacy in Science

Bring Science Alive! is aligned with the Common Core State Standards for English Language Arts & Literacy (CCELA). Literacy instruction is built into the online Student Text, Interactive Student Notebook, and the Lesson Presentations. The following six key points are from the grades 6–8 CCELA Standards for Literacy in History/Social Studies, Science, and Technical Subjects. They are particularly important in science instruction.

Reading Standards for Literacy

✓ **Main Ideas and Details**
Identifying key ideas and details applies to reading science text, following multistep procedures for experiments, and using scientific tools and other technology.

When using the *Bring Science Alive!* online text, students have the option to see the main idea of each section highlighted. Additionally, every lesson includes one or more multistep investigations that students must follow to carry out science experiments, analyze data, and solve engineering problems.

✓ **Craft and Structure** In the middle grades, mastering new vocabulary includes understanding the meaning of scientific and mathematical symbols as well as domain-specific terms, words, and phrases.

Learning of scientific symbols and mathematical representations is scaffolded in *Bring Science Alive!* First, the concept is presented in words and phrases. Next, symbols are shown alongside these words and phrases. Finally, the symbolic notation is shown on its own.

✓ **Integration of Knowledge and Ideas** Students should be able to integrate their learning on a topic using experiments, multimedia materials, and the text.

Each *Bring Science Alive!* lesson concludes with a processing task that requires students to demonstrate their understanding of science and engineering practices, crosscutting concepts, and disciplinary core ideas as a result of carrying out investigations, manipulating simulations, and reading the text.

Writing Standards for Literacy

✓ **Purposes for Writing** The writing standards stress the use of certain conventions of good writing, including the use of previews, supporting details, appropriate transitions, domain-specific vocabulary, and an objective tone.

Bring Science Alive! students write for different purposes, including to explain scientific concepts and to record investigation procedures and results so that others can replicate and test them. Students are asked to construct written arguments to persuade others to accept an engineering design solution. They also write accounts of their investigations using precise language, scientific vocabulary, and minimal bias.

✓ **Production and Distribution of Writing** Routine writing of clear and coherent content that is appropriate to its purpose is central throughout the writing standards.

Bring Science Alive! includes regular writing opportunities in the Lesson Presentations and Interactive Student Notebook. Writing, peer review, and editing are essential tools in guiding students to develop arguments and explanations that result in three dimensional learning.

✓ **Research to Build and Present Knowledge** Short research projects, using a variety of print and digital sources appropriately, should be carried out to answer broad questions that generate more specific questions.

Students build research skills using print and digital sources, including the Internet. Unit problems require students to gather and assess relevant information and to integrate this information with what they learn during hands-on investigations.

Considerate Text

Literacy is fundamental for success in science. *Bring Science Alive!* is both engaging and helps students read text that is more complex and at a higher level than other text they read. That's because our writers wrote it as "considerate text," which is another way to say that it makes readers want to read it. Considerate text is well-written and well-organized. Here are some ways this Student Text is considerate of all levels of readers.

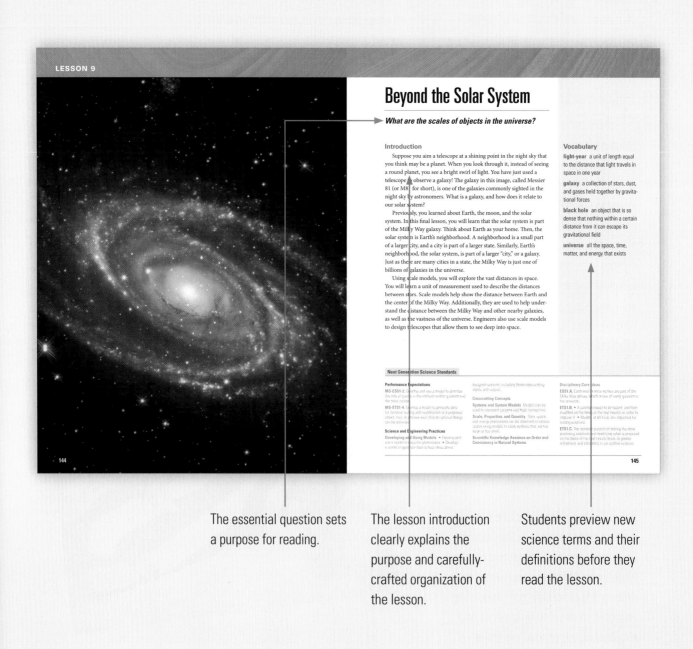

The essential question sets a purpose for reading.

The lesson introduction clearly explains the purpose and carefully-crafted organization of the lesson.

Students preview new science terms and their definitions before they read the lesson.

Short sections, each with an informative title, make it easier for readers to understand and remember the main ideas.

The paragraph that begins each section orients and engages the reader.

Single-column text makes the lesson easier to read.

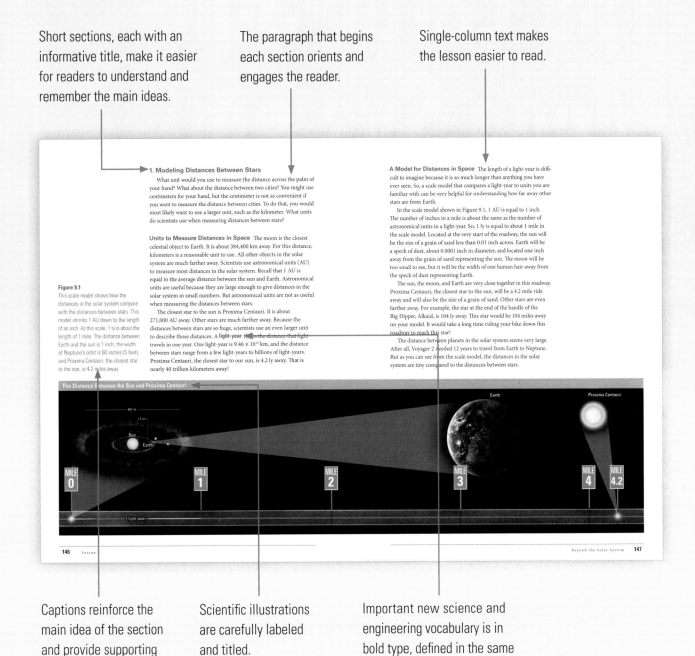

1. Modeling Distances Between Stars

What unit would you use to measure the distance across the palm of your hand? What about the distance between two cities? You might use centimeters for your hand, but the centimeter is not as convenient if you want to measure the distance between cities. To do that, you would most likely want to use a larger unit, such as the kilometer. What units do scientists use when measuring distances between stars?

Units to Measure Distances in Space The moon is the closest celestial object to Earth. It is about 384,400 km away. For this distance, kilometers is a reasonable unit to use. All other objects in the solar system are much farther away. Scientists use astronomical units (AU) to measure most distances in the solar system. Recall that 1 AU is equal to the average distance between the sun and Earth. Astronomical units are useful because they are large enough to give distances in the solar system in small numbers. But astronomical units are not as useful when measuring the distances between stars.

The closest star to the sun is Proxima Centauri. It is about 271,000 AU away. Other stars are much farther away. Because the distances between stars are so huge, scientists use an even larger unit to describe those distances. A **light-year (ly)** is the distance that light travels in one year. One light-year is 9.46×10^{12} km, and the distance between stars range from a few light-years to billions of light-years. Proxima Centauri, the closest star to our sun, is 4.2 ly away. That is nearly 40 trillion kilometers away!

A Model for Distances in Space The length of a light-year is difficult to imagine because it is so much longer than anything you have ever seen. So, a scale model that compares a light-year to units you are familiar with can be very helpful for understanding how far away other stars are from Earth.

In the scale model shown in Figure 9.1, 1 AU is equal to 1 inch. The number of inches in a mile is about the same as the number of astronomical units in a light-year. So, 1 ly is equal to about 1 mile in the scale model. Located at the very start of the roadway, the sun will be the size of a grain of sand less than 0.01 inch across. Earth will be a speck of dust, about 0.0001 inch in diameter, and located one inch away from the grain of sand representing the sun. The moon will be too small to see, but it will be the width of one human hair away from the speck of dust representing Earth.

The sun, the moon, and Earth are very close together in this roadway. Proxima Centauri, the closest star to the sun, will be a 4.2 mile ride away and will also be the size of a grain of sand. Other stars are even farther away. For example, the star at the end of the handle of the Big Dipper, Alkaid, is 104 ly away. This star would be 104 miles away on your model. It would take a long time riding your bike down this roadway to reach this star!

The distance between planets in the solar system seems very large. After all, Voyager 2 needed 12 years to travel from Earth to Neptune. But as you can see from the scale model, the distances in the solar system are tiny compared to the distances between stars.

Figure 9.1
This scale model shows how the distances in the solar system compare with the distances between stars. This model shrinks 1 AU down to the length of an inch. At this scale, 1 ly is about the length of 1 mile. The distance between Earth and the sun is 1 inch, the width of Neptune's orbit is 60 inches (5 feet), and Proxima Centauri, the closest star to the sun, is 4.2 miles away.

The Distance Between the Sun and Proxima Centauri

60 in
1 in
Sun
Earth
Earth
Proxima Centauri
1 light year

MILE 0
MILE 1
MILE 2
MILE 3
MILE 4
MILE 4.2

Captions reinforce the main idea of the section and provide supporting details.

Scientific illustrations are carefully labeled and titled.

Important new science and engineering vocabulary is in bold type, defined in the same sentence, and used throughout the rest of the text.

The Earth-Sun-Moon System

OVERVIEW

One day, you use a pinhole camera to look into the sky. The sun slowly "disappears" for a few minutes before reappearing bit by bit. What just happened? In this unit, you will discover how patterns that you see in the sky, such as eclipses, are related to the position of Earth, the sun, and the moon as they are oriented in space. As you read about these patterns, you will also model them in your classroom planetarium. Finally, you will work in groups to produce a video that will teach adults about these patterns in the sky.

UNIT CONTENTS

Performance Assessment
Use what you learned about the Earth-sun-moon system to develop a model, and use it to create a film that educates adults on a pattern that can be observed from Earth.

UNIT 1

Next Generation Science Standards

Performance Expectations

MS-ESS1-1. Develop and use a model of the Earth-sun-moon system to describe the cyclic patterns of lunar phases, eclipses of the sun and moon, and seasons.

MS-ETS1-1. Define the criteria and constraints of a design problem with sufficient precision to ensure a successful solution, taking into account relevant scientific principles and potential impacts on people and the natural environment that may limit possible solutions.

Science and Engineering Practices

Developing and Using Models
Develop and use a model to describe phenomena.

Asking Questions and Defining Problems
Define a design problem that can be solved through the development of an object, tool, process or system and includes multiple criteria and constraints, including scientific knowledge that may limit possible solutions.

Crosscutting Concepts

Patterns
Patterns can be used to identify cause and effect relationships.

Connections to Nature of Science:
Scientific Knowledge Assumes an Order and Consistency in Natural Systems
Science assumes that objects and events in natural systems occur in consistent patterns that are understandable through measurement and observation.

Influence of Science, Engineering, and Technology on Society and the Natural World
• All human activity draws on natural resources and has both short and long-term consequences, positive as well as negative, for the health of people and the natural environment. • The uses of technologies and limitations on their use are driven by individual or societal needs, desires, and values; by the findings of scientific research; and by differences in such factors as climate, natural resources, and economic conditions.

Disciplinary Core Ideas

ESS1.A. The Universe and Its Stars
Patterns of the apparent motion of the sun, the moon, and stars in the sky can be observed, described, predicted, and explained with models.

ESS1.B. Earth and the Solar System
This model of the solar system can explain eclipses of the sun and the moon. Earth's spin axis is fixed in direction over the short-term but tilted relative to its orbit around the sun. The seasons are a result of that tilt and are caused by the differential intensity of sunlight on different areas of Earth across the year.

ETS1.A. Defining and Delimiting Engineering Problems
The more precisely a design task's criteria and constraints can be defined, the more likely it is that the designed solution will be successful. Specification of constraints includes consideration of scientific principles and other relevant knowledge that are likely to limit possible solutions.

Connect Your Learning

What does the Earth-sun-moon system mean, and how does it affect you? You, as somebody on Earth, are part of the Earth-sun-moon system. All of the patterns you see in the sky are a result of these three celestial bodies moving in space and appearing in different orientations. Understanding these three celestial bodies helps you connect many seemingly unrelated phenomena you observe from Earth.

The sun rises toward the east and travels across the sky to set toward the west every single day. But the sun does not always follow the exact same path. If you use a pinhole camera, you can take a picture over the course of six months. How does the tilt of Earth's axis affect the sun's path in the sky?

The Earth-Sun-Moon System

Some nights you go out and the moon seems to light up the sky. Other nights, the moon provides little or no light. Over the course of about a month, the moon appears to change shape, growing from a crescent shape to a round circle and then shrinking back down to a crescent shape. How does the moon's location in space explain this phenomenon?

In 1969, scientists and engineers made it possible for a human to walk on the surface of the moon for the first time. How did their careful determination of criteria and constraints help them achieve this amazing feat of engineering?

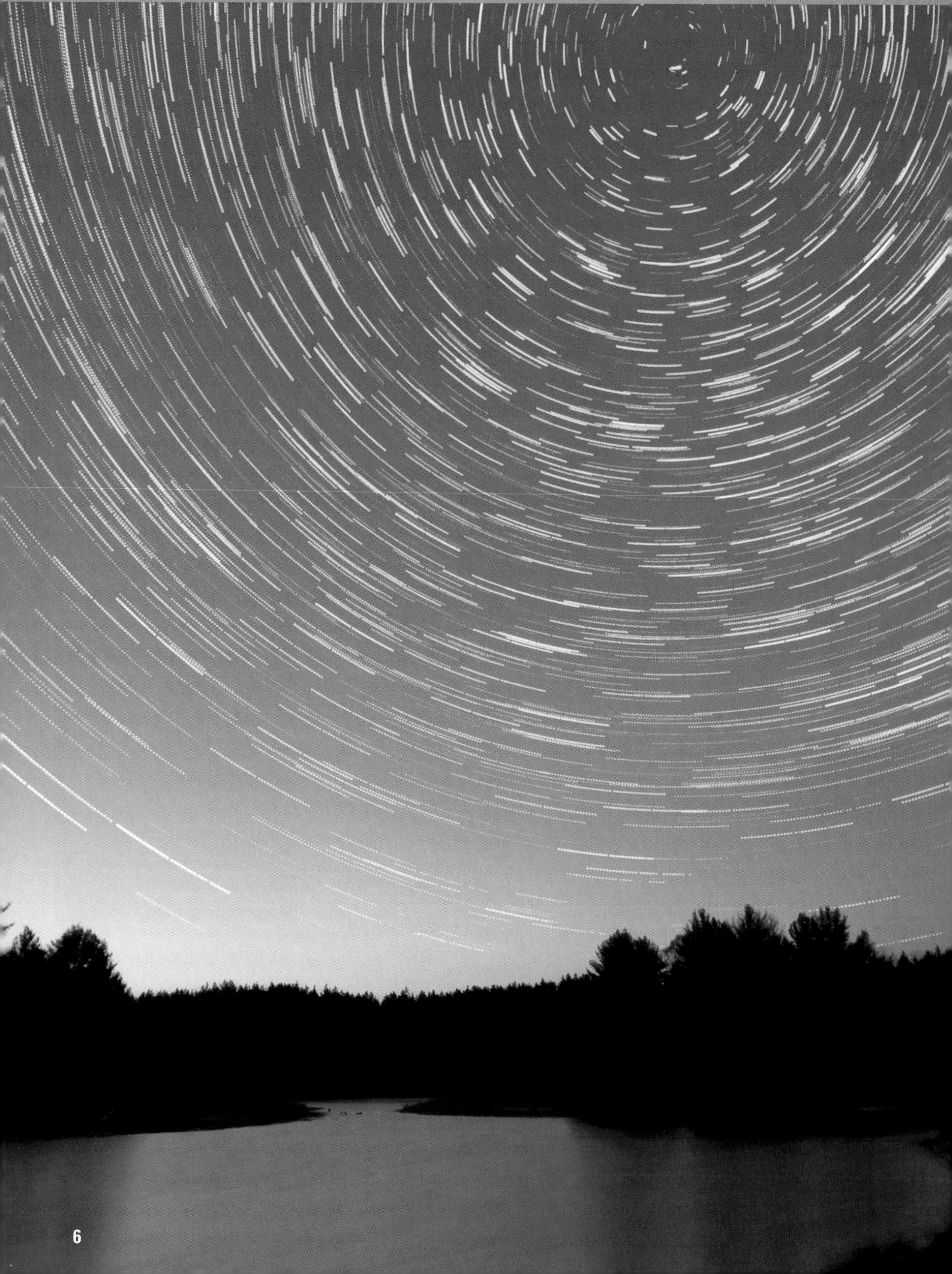

Earth's Rotation and Revolution

Why do the stars and sun appear and move across the sky?

Introduction

Stars fill the night sky like tiny pinpricks of light against darkness. But unlike the stars you may observe on a clear night, the stars photographed here are not tiny dots of light. Instead, the stars appear as curved lines revolving around a single point. Why? The photo was taken over the course of a night. As time passed, the stars moved in the sky, causing them to appear as curved streaks, or star trails. But these trails are not a jumbled mess; a pattern can be observed. They curve in neat circles around a single point, near the star Polaris, which is also called the North Star.

Stars are not the only objects in the sky that seem to move in patterns. Every day, the sun rises toward the east, appears to move across the sky, and sets toward the west. Observing and describing patterns is an essential way that scientists explore the natural world.

In this lesson, you will begin to study the relationship between Earth and other objects in space and how these motions cause the patterns you can observe in the sky. For example, the patterns of motion of the sun and the stars result mostly from the rotation of Earth. Finally, you will learn what makes some of the stars in the photo special and why they appear to move in circles.

Next Generation Science Standards

Performance Expectations

MS-ESS1-1. Develop and use a model of the Earth-sun-moon system to describe the cyclic patterns of lunar phases, eclipses of the sun and moon, and seasons.

MS-ETS1-1. Define the criteria and constraints of a design problem with sufficient precision to ensure a successful solution, taking into account relevant scientific principles and potential impacts on people and the natural environment that may limit possible solutions.

Science and Engineering Practices

Developing and Using Models Develop and use a model to describe phenomena.

Asking Questions and Defining Problems
Define a design problem that can be solved through the development of an object, tool, process or system and includes multiple criteria and constraints, including scientific knowledge that may limit possible solutions.

Crosscutting Concepts

Patterns Patterns can be used to identify cause and effect relationships.

Influence of Science, Engineering, and Technology on Society and the Natural World

Scientific Knowledge Assumes an Order and Consistency in Natural Systems

Disciplinary Core Ideas

ESS1.A. Patterns of the apparent motion of the sun, the moon, and stars in the sky can be observed, described, predicted, and explained with models.

ETS1.A. The more precisely a design task's criteria and constraints can be defined, the more likely it is that the designed solution will be successful. Specification of constraints includes consideration of scientific principles and other relevant knowledge that are likely to limit possible solutions.

1. Earth's Rotation

If you filmed the night sky over several hours, you would notice the stars moving. They would make vibrant star trails in circles around a central point. This point is near a star called Polaris, or the North Star. Stars are not the only objects that move in the sky. The sun, for example, also moves across the sky over the course of a day. What causes the stars and the sun to move?

Picture yourself standing on a baseball field like the one shown in Figure 1.1A. Home plate is on the north side of the field, and second base is on the south side. When you stand on the pitcher's mound and look directly above you, you would see the sun rise toward the east, above third base. The sun would travel directly above you, across the sky, until it sets toward the west, above first base. Although the sun may not rise exactly due east or set due west, the overall pattern of the sun rising in the east and setting in the west does not change.

The stars, sun, and moon are all called celestial objects. A **celestial object** is an object in space that is not placed there by humans. The stars, the sun, the moon, and even the planets are all celestial objects. From Earth, celestial objects appear to move across the sky every day and every night. However, it is usually not their motion that we see; it is Earth's!

If many celestial objects do not move, why do we observe them traveling across the sky? In this case, it is because you are standing on Earth, a moving object; this is one example of a cause and effect relationship, where one event causes another to happen. Suppose you were riding on a carousel in a park. When you look out, you would see the rest of the park spinning in circles. The park is not actually spinning in circles; rather, you are! Similarly, the celestial objects in space appear to move daily in circular patterns because of Earth's spin.

Figure 1.1A

Each day, the sun appears to rise and set. If you were standing on the pitcher's mound, facing south, you would see the sun rise toward the east, toward third base. After traveling across the sky, the sun sets toward the west, toward first base.

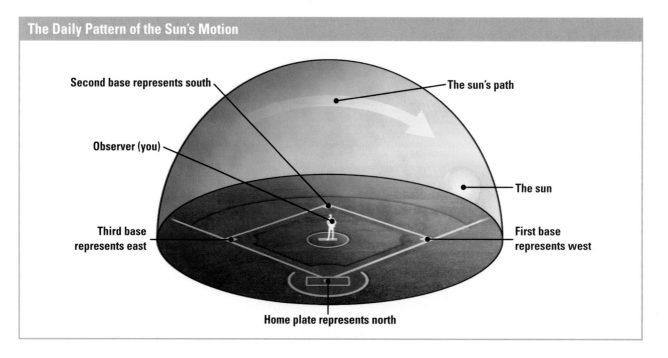

The Daily Pattern of the Sun's Motion

Second base represents south

The sun's path

Observer (you)

The sun

Third base represents east

First base represents west

Home plate represents north

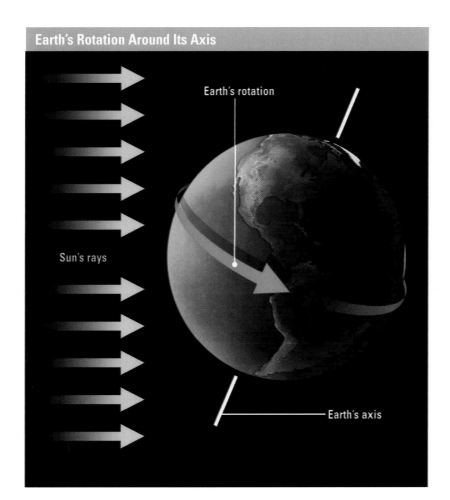

Earth's Rotation Around Its Axis

Earth's rotation

Sun's rays

Earth's axis

Rotation is the spin of an object around a point or a line. The point or line an object rotates around is called its **axis**. A carousel's axis is the metal pole that the platform spins around. Earth does not have a metal pole protruding from its center. Instead, it has an imaginary line that it rotates around. Figure 1.1B shows Earth's axis as it connects the North and South Pole, and goes through the center of the planet.

Earth's rotation is the process that causes the sun to appear to rise and set, even though the sun hardly moves at all. Suppose you are standing in the baseball field in Figure 1.1A. At dawn, Earth rotates and you turn towards the sun, and you observe the sun appear above third base. Throughout the morning, Earth continues to rotate until noon, when the baseball field is facing the sun. The sun appears above second base. After noon, Earth begins to turn away from the sun until dusk, when the sun appears to set over first base.

Likewise, the stars appear to move across the sky due to Earth's rotation. During the night, Earth continues to rotate. The stars become visible at night as you face away from the sun. Throughout the night, you observe star trails as the stars appear to move in concentric circles around Polaris. However these stars are actually almost stationary in space. Instead, your position changes in relation to these stars as Earth rotates. This causes the stars to appear to move in the sky.

2. Earth's Revolution

Suppose you stood on the pitcher's mound of a baseball field to observe the night sky for many months. What would you see? Each night you would see the stars travel in a circle around Polaris because of Earth's rotation. But you would also notice that they seem to be slowly travelling from east to west across the sky as the months pass. If stars don't actually move, what might be causing this effect?

To answer your question, you decide to track the stars for a whole year. In October, in the Northern Hemisphere, the constellation Orion is rising in the east above the horizon at around the same time the sun sets. It travels across the sky over the course of the night and moves below the horizon in the west at around the same time the sun rises. In January, Orion is high in the sky when the sun sets. It moves across the sky and sets in the west sometime around midnight. By March, Orion is setting in the west around the same time the sun sets. It is not visible at all during the night. When you get back to October, Orion is rising when the sun sets again, so you can see it.

During the time that Orion no longer appears in the night sky, other stars do. The stars in the constellation Scorpius start rising in the east above the horizon in May. Just like Orion's stars, Scorpius' stars move across the sky over the course of many months before setting, but these stars set in August.

Since Orion and Scorpius are only visible during certain times of the year, the stars in these constellations are called seasonal stars. Just as each season only occurs for part of the year, seasonal stars only appear in the night sky for a portion of the year. Sometimes, seasonal stars are called summer or winter stars depending on which season you see them.

Figure 1.2A

Different stars are visible at different times of the year. In the winter, Orion is visible from the Northern Hemisphere. As time passes, Orion slowly shifts downwards towards the horizon. By the summer, Orion is no longer visible in the sky. Instead, the constellation Scorpius is.

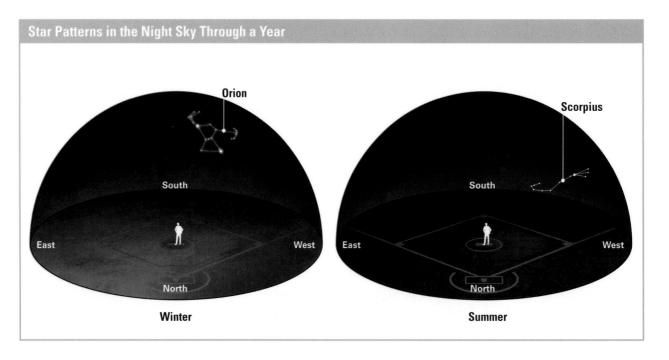

Star Patterns in the Night Sky Through a Year

Orion

South

East

West

North

Winter

Scorpius

South

East

West

North

Summer

You observe the pattern of seasonal stars because Earth travels around the sun once every year. The motion of an object around another object in space is called **revolution**. Earth is in revolution around the sun. You might also say that Earth revolves around the sun.

The path that the revolving object follows is called its **orbit**. All orbits have the shape of an ellipse, which is an oval shape. Ellipses vary in shape; they can be circular, a long and skinny oval, or something in-between. Earth's orbit is almost a circle.

How does Earth's orbit result in seasonal stars? Compared to Earth's motion, stars have a fixed position in space, so they do not move. As Earth revolves around the sun, the stars change in their relative position to Earth. When the stars are in the same direction from Earth as the sun, they are no longer visible in the sky at night. If you try to look at the stars in that direction, you cannot see them. The stars are in the sky during the day, but the sun's light is so bright that the light from those stars are not visible from Earth.

In January, the sun and Scorpius are in the same direction from Earth. You cannot see Scorpius in January because it is in the sky during the day, and the sun's light is so bright it makes Scorpius not visible. However, as Earth revolves around the sun, Scorpius ends up being in the opposite direction as the sun from Earth. When you look in Scorpius' direction, you are looking into the night sky. Then, you can see the stars of Scorpius.

Figure 1.2B
Earth revolves around the sun in its orbit. Stars have fixed positions and are only visible when they are in a direction opposite from the sun, so they are not being drowned out by the sun's light.

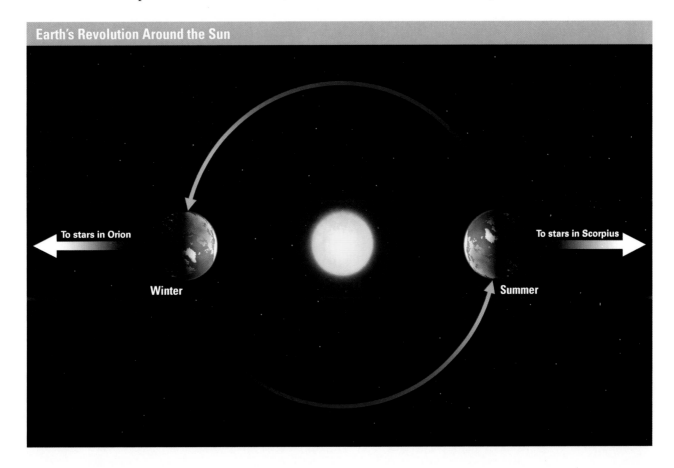

Earth's Revolution Around the Sun

To stars in Orion

Winter

To stars in Scorpius

Summer

Patterns of the Sun and Stars Due to Earth's Rotation and Revolution

From Earth, you can observe celestial objects moving in two patterns in the sky. Each pattern is the result of a different cause and effect relationship. The pattern you see over the course of a day is due to Earth's rotation, and the patterns you can see over the course of a year is due to Earth's revolution.

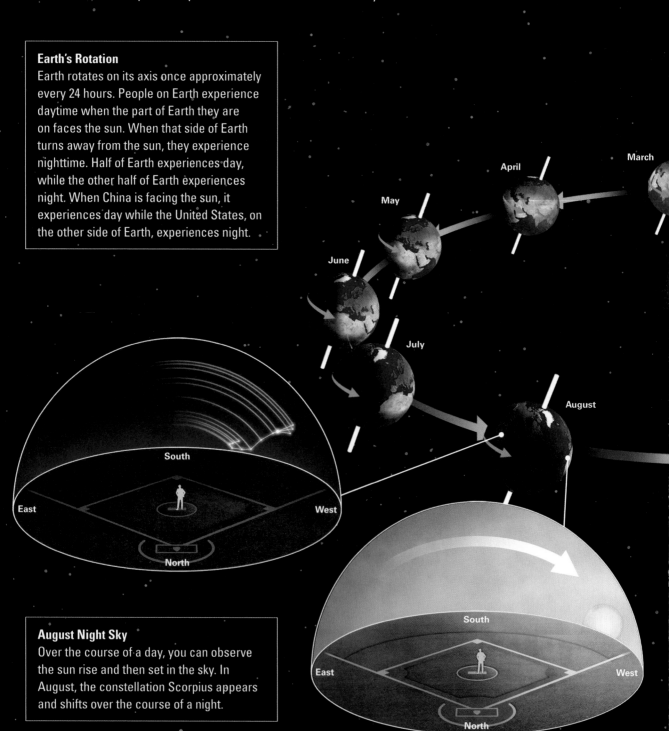

Earth's Rotation
Earth rotates on its axis once approximately every 24 hours. People on Earth experience daytime when the part of Earth they are on faces the sun. When that side of Earth turns away from the sun, they experience nighttime. Half of Earth experiences day, while the other half of Earth experiences night. When China is facing the sun, it experiences day while the United States, on the other side of Earth, experiences night.

August Night Sky
Over the course of a day, you can observe the sun rise and then set in the sky. In August, the constellation Scorpius appears and shifts over the course of a night.

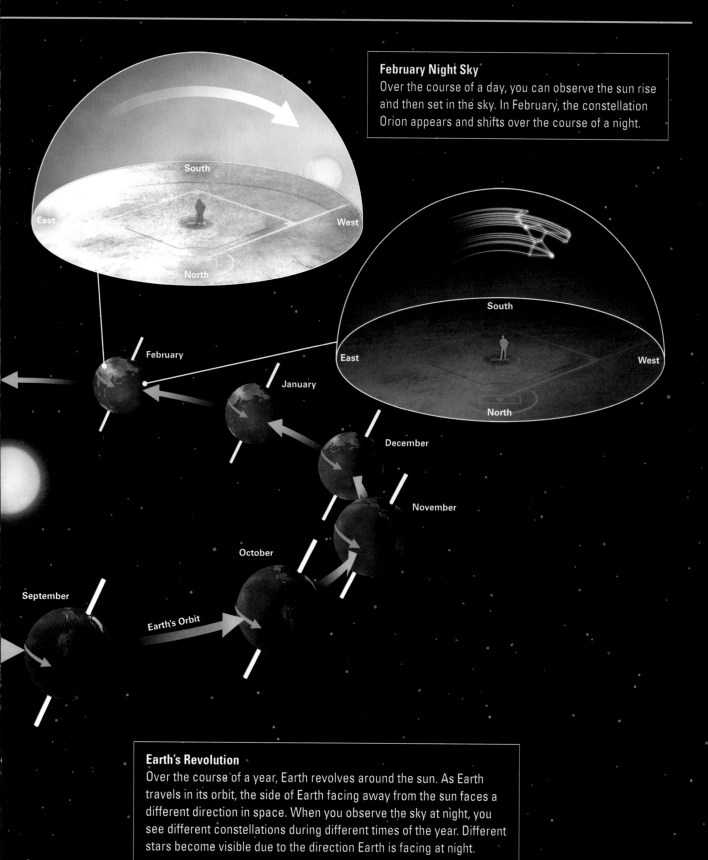

February Night Sky
Over the course of a day, you can observe the sun rise and then set in the sky. In February, the constellation Orion appears and shifts over the course of a night.

South

East

West

North

February

January

South

East

West

December

North

November

October

September

Earth's Orbit

Earth's Revolution
Over the course of a year, Earth revolves around the sun. As Earth travels in its orbit, the side of Earth facing away from the sun faces a different direction in space. When you observe the sky at night, you see different constellations during different times of the year. Different stars become visible due to the direction Earth is facing at night.

3. Earth's Orbital Plane

The stars of Orion and Scorpius are seasonal because of Earth's revolution. However, depending on where you are observing the sky, there are stars that do not rise and set like Orion and Scorpius. Rather than rising, moving across the sky, and setting, these stars move in a circle around Polaris. They never get low enough to dip below the horizon. These same stars can be seen all year round. What makes them visible when other stars are seasonal?

These stars are visible because they are located high above the plane that contains Earth's orbit. A plane is a flat surface that extends forever. Earth's orbit is on one plane, called Earth's **orbital plane**. Just as you can trace an ellipse on the flat surface of a desk, you could trace Earth's orbit on the flat surface of the plane it rests on.

Celestial Objects on Earth's Orbital Plane Some celestial objects lie on or near Earth's orbital plane, including the sun and the seasonal stars. Since the sun lies on Earth's orbital plane, you can only see it when you are on the side of Earth that is facing the sun. At night, you are facing away from the sun. If you wanted to see it, you would have to look through Earth.

Likewise, seasonal stars lie on, or near, Earth's orbital plane. When you look out into space at night, you are always looking out at space in the opposite direction of the sun. As Earth travels in its orbit on its orbital plane, the direction you would have to gaze to see night changes. You see different stars because you are looking at a different region of space. As Earth revolves around the sun, different stars become visible during different times of the year. At other times, your view of these stars is obscured by the sun on Earth's orbital plane.

Figure 1.3A
Some objects sit on Earth's orbital plane. The sun, Earth's orbit and the seasonal stars all lie on or near Earth's orbital plane.

Earth's Orbit and Earth's Orbital Plane

Earth's Orbit

Orbital Plane

Celestial Objects Far from Earth's Orbital Plane Not all stars lie on or near Earth's orbital plane. Some stars lie far away from Earth's orbital plane in the direction of Earth's axis as it extends far into space. These stars are called circumpolar stars. *Circumpolar* means something travels around one of Earth's poles. **Circumpolar stars** are stars located above and around Earth's north and south poles. You can see circumpolar stars all year round because they are never drowned out by the sun's light. Since they reside above the orbital plane, you have a line of sight to them no matter when in the year it is.

When you observe the sky over the course of a night, you can see stars rotating around Polaris. These stars are circumpolar stars and are visible all year round. Polaris is located close to the North Pole. For that reason, Polaris is sometimes also called the North Star. However, Polaris and the stars that circle it are not visible from the South Pole. Just as seasonal stars are not visible when they are blocked by the sun, most circumpolar stars that reside above the North Pole are not visible from the Southern Hemisphere because they are being blocked by Earth. Circumpolar stars that reside in the direction of the South Pole are not visible from the Northern Hemisphere.

Figure 1.3B

Circumpolar stars are located above and around Earth's north and south poles. They are visible all year round because they are above Earth's orbital plane and are never drowned out by the sun's light.

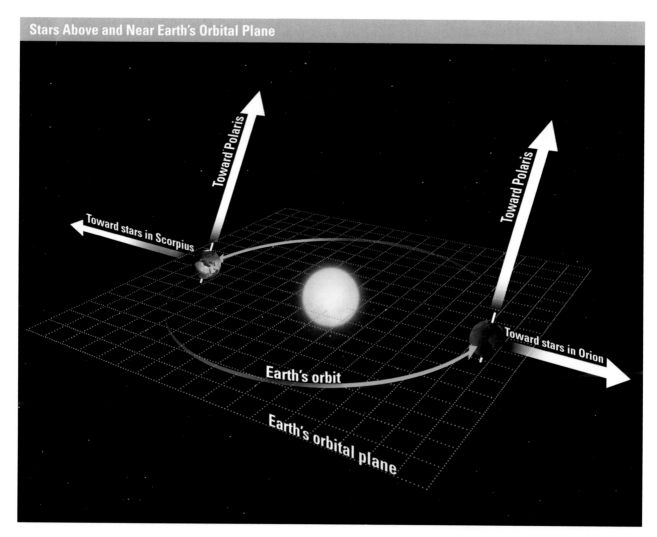

Stars Above and Near Earth's Orbital Plane

Toward Polaris

Toward stars in Scorpius

Toward Polaris

Toward stars in Orion

Earth's orbit

Earth's orbital plane

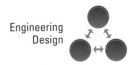

4. Solving the Problem of Locating Stars

Have you ever used an app to identify a star in the night sky? Some apps can be held up in front of you and exactly recreate the night sky on the screen. They show stars, and perhaps the moon and planets if they are visible. How did software engineers design the apps to know where all the stars are at a specific date and time during the year?

Defining the Problem Precisely It is difficult to track the position of the stars because of their apparent motions. Where a star is located in the sky depends on Earth's position in its orbit and your location on Earth's surface. Some stars are only visible during certain times of the year. Over the course of a night, stars appear to follow a circular path around Polaris. All of these apparent motions make it difficult to determine exactly where you will see each star at a particular time.

A lot of computational power would be required to calculate the position of every star based on Earth's position in its orbit, your location on Earth's surface, and the current time. App engineers are *constrained* by the speed at which smartphones can calculate the positions of stars. A **constraint** is a limitation on an engineering solution. Engineers know that people will only use their app if it loads quickly. The engineers must limit the amount of computing power needed to calculate and display the night sky quickly.

Yet the app must meet the *criteria* of displaying the night sky quickly and correctly from anywhere on Earth. **Criteria** are the requirements that must be met for an engineering solution to be successful. Engineers must be precise about their criteria and constraints to overcome any challenges. How can the app determine the position of all the stars and still load quickly?

To develop a smartphone application that can display the night sky quickly and correctly from anywhere on Earth, engineers must define the criteria and constraints precisely.

A Solution Using the Celestial Sphere To locate stars, astronomers created a model that placed Earth inside an imaginary sphere, called the celestial sphere. Celestial objects are placed on the surface of the sphere, and their location corresponds with what you would see at night. Just like using latitude and longitude to describe the location of cities and monuments on Earth, astronomers created a grid to describe the location of celestial objects. The celestial sphere is like a map of the night sky, showing the location of constellations.

Using the celestial sphere model in the app software would help meet all the criteria defined for the problem of locating stars. The latitude and longitude on the celestial sphere do not change with time of day or time of night and are the same for any place on Earth. And the celestial sphere model is simple enough that it will not make an app load slowly. As a result, anyone on Earth can use the system at any time. Astronomers even use the system to figure out when the celestial objects that they are studying are going to be in the night sky.

By defining their criteria and constraints precisely, engineers can come up with a solution that solves their engineering problem. Using the celestial sphere in the app software meets the criteria and constraints of the problem.

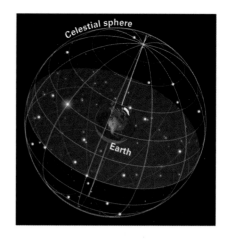

By defining their criteria and constraints precisely, engineers could use a system similar to latitude and longitude to mark the locations of stars. This system, called the celestial sphere, could help them create a smartphone app.

LESSON SUMMARY

Earth's Rotation and Revolution

Earth's Rotation Earth rotates around its axis over the course of a day. As a result, celestial objects in the sky appear to move throughout a day and a night. Earth's rotation causes nearly unmoving objects, such as the sun and other stars, to appear to move in the night sky.

Earth's Revolution Earth revolves around the sun over the course of a year. Different stars are visible in the night sky over the course of a year due to the direction of night changing as Earth moves around the sun. Different constellations are visible depending on the time of the year because of the orientation of Earth and the sun in space.

Earth's Orbital Plane Earth, the sun, and the seasonal stars are located on a plane. A plane is a flat surface that stretches on forever. As a result, the seasonal stars are only visible when not obscured by other objects on Earth's orbital plane, such as the sun or the sun's light. Circumpolar stars sit above or below Earth's orbital plane, so they are visible all year round because they are not drowned out by the sun's light.

Solving the Problem of Locating Stars To develop software that allows people to quickly identify stars in the sky, engineers must consider the criteria and constraints of their problem.

Astronomy Needs You

At every moment of every day, telescopes are taking images of objects in space. They gather so much information that professional astronomers cannot analyze it all. That's why astronomy needs you! What can you, a middle school student, do to advance astronomy? You'd be surprised!

In 2010, astronomers asked for help classifying hundreds of thousands of images taken by a telescope in space. People all over the world volunteered to use their own computers to view and mark the images. Astronomers asked the volunteers to look for specific things, but the volunteers soon noticed other objects that kept showing up in the images. The volunteers called the objects "yellow balls" and wondered what they were. The questions about the yellow balls got the attention of the astronomers in charge of the project. The astronomers studied the balls and found that they were a previously unknown step in the development of very large stars.

The volunteers who noticed and inquired about the yellow balls are just some of many amateur astronomers who have made discoveries and contributions to science. Amateur astronomers are people who are interested in space but do not pursue astronomy full-time or as a profession.

Amateur astronomers were the first to notice unusual yellow balls in photos taken by a space telescope. Their discovery helped professional astronomers learn more about how stars form.

Anyone can become an amateur astronomer as long as they carefully observe the universe and think about their observations. While some amateur astronomers have years of training and education in astronomy, most others do not. The person who discovered the planet Uranus was a musician. A science writer named David Levy has found more than 20 comets, including the comet that crashed into Jupiter in 1994. Amateur astronomers don't even have to be adults; people as young as 10 and 14 have discovered amazing things like supernovas!

Some amateur astronomers become famous after their discoveries, but other amateur astronomers are famous for other reasons. One of Abraham Lincoln's sons, a former mayor of Manchester, England, a German Princess, and even a British movie star were all amateur astronomers.

A Stargazing Star

Will Hay was a popular British comedian who acted in plays and movies in the 1930s and 1940s. He played schoolteachers or police officers that were not very intelligent and not very good at their jobs. In real life, Hay was nothing like the characters he played; he was smart and interested in learning. He was particularly interested in astronomy and owned large telescopes that he kept in his backyard. Hay liked to use his telescopes to observe the planets, and like any good scientist, he wrote very detailed notes about his observations.

In August 1933, Hay saw an unusual, large, white spot on Saturn's surface. He carefully wrote his observations in his logbook and drew a sketch of what he saw. Although Hay was not the only one to see the white spot, his finding made the news, and his fame grew.

Hay continued to observe the white spot several times over another month and a half; he noted changes in the spot's shape and size and proposed possible causes for the spot. Scientists now know that the spot was a huge storm in Saturn's atmosphere and that similar storms appear about every 30 years. Although Hay was an amateur astronomer, he attended astronomy meetings and sometimes presented speeches at those meetings. He continued to watch the skies and was greatly respected by professional astronomers.

These 2011 photos of Saturn show white spots similar to the one observed by the popular British star Will Hay in 1933. Spots, like the ones in these photos, are huge storms in Saturn's atmosphere that develop about every 30 years.

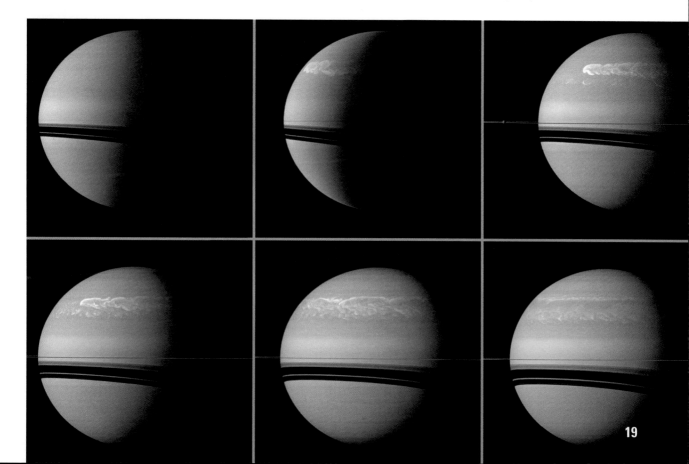

Armchair Astronomy

Will Hay did his astronomy research by looking through his own powerful telescopes. Most people do not own such telescopes, but that does not mean that they cannot help scientists with their research. Almost all astronomy research today is done on computers, and anyone with a computer and Internet access can help out.

Several websites are set up for amateur astronomers to participate in astronomy research. To take part in most of these projects, you go through training to learn what to look for. The training is usually short, and you can get to work right away. For example, a recent project that amateur astronomers worked on was a moon-mapping project. Training for this project was a video that showed how to use a computer mouse to mark craters in photos of the moon's surface.

Thousands of amateur astronomers work on these computer projects, and several people analyze each image. Therefore, as long as you follow the instructions carefully, you don't have to worry about making mistakes. Computers compare the work of everyone who saw a particular image to deduce an accurate result.

If you work on these computer projects, you can work whenever you want; you don't have to wait for nightfall. You also can do your work wherever you want—you could sit at a desk or in a comfortable armchair.

Amateur astronomers can use computers to help scientists analyze data. A better map of the moon's surface was made possible through the work of amateur astronomers.

Outdoor Observations

Although computer astronomy can be easy to do, a lot of the fun of doing astronomy is looking up in the sky and witnessing celestial phenomena with your own eyes. A photograph of an eclipse is interesting, but seeing an eclipse in person can be even more exhilarating.

Some of the amateur astronomy projects found on the Internet do require volunteers to do some stargazing. For these projects, you must go online to download star charts and instructions on what to do and what to look for. Then you can observe the requested stars or other celestial objects at night and write down the details about what you see. Later, you must go back online to report your results.

You can be an amateur astronomer without working on a project. You can start observing on your own with just a star chart. The chart will allow you to identify the objects that you see. Star charts printed on thin plastic or cardboard are inexpensive and easy to use. Star chart apps for mobile devices are often even cheaper, and although they may take practice to use, they can be very effective and very helpful.

Another way to be involved in amateur astronomy is to join an astronomy club in your community. Astronomy clubs have meetings where you can learn about various space topics. They also have viewing parties during which people bring telescopes and binoculars for everyone to use. Experienced amateur and professional astronomers help new members find interesting celestial objects and instruct them to use different kinds of observing tools.

Becoming an amateur astronomer is easy, and you can be involved in so many different ways. No matter how you choose to participate, all you need are your eyes and a few tools such as a computer or mobile device or a star chart. Who knows? Maybe you will see something that no one has noticed before. If your discovery is big enough, you might become as famous as Will Hay. Keep looking up, because astronomy needs you! ◆

If you go to an astronomy club's viewing party, you may get an opportunity to look through a powerful telescope. Astronomy clubs help amateur astronomers learn more about the stars and other objects in space.

Earth's Tilted Axis

Why are there different seasons?

Introduction

The weather is warm in spring and trees begin to grow new leaves. Then, summer comes, hot and bright. The weather cools off in autumn, and some trees begin to lose their leaves. Before long, it is winter, the coldest time of the year. The pattern of the seasons continues as the weather warms up and spring occurs again.

A change in temperature is just one pattern that occurs with the change in seasons. What other patterns can you observe over the course of a year? You may notice that the sun is in the sky for more time each day during the summer. In the winter, the days are shorter because the sun is not in the sky for as long. You may also notice that the sun travels higher above the horizon during the summer than during the winter. Are there any other patterns that you have observed? How does the orientation of the Earth relative to the sun cause these seasonal patterns?

So far, you have learned about patterns of celestial objects and how they are caused by Earth's motion. In this lesson, you will continue to explore some cause and effect relationships related to patterns you can observe on Earth's surface.

You will first get an overview of the many seasonal patterns observed on Earth. Then, you will learn how the angle of sunlight hitting Earth causes uneven heating of Earth's surface. Next, you will explore how Earth's axis is tilted and how this tilt causes seasonal patterns. Finally, you will read about how the sun's path in the sky changes over the course of a year and that ancient people tracked changes in the sun's path to monitor the seasons.

Vocabulary

system a set of connected parts that form a complex whole

solstice a time of year when the sun is directly overhead at one of the tropics during noon

tropic the latitudes furthest north and south that receive sunlight at a perpendicular angle

equinox a time of year when the sun is directly overhead at the equator at noon, when day and night are of equal length

---

Next Generation Science Standards

Performance Expectations
MS-ESS1-1. Develop and use a model of the Earth-sun-moon system to describe the cyclic patterns of lunar phases, eclipses of the sun and moon, and seasons.

Science and Engineering Practices
Developing and Using Models Develop and use a model to describe phenomena.

Crosscutting Concepts
Patterns Patterns can be used to identify cause and effect relationships.
Scientific Knowledge Assumes an Order and Consistency in Natural Systems

Disciplinary Core Ideas
ESS1.A. Patterns of the apparent motion of the sun, the moon, and stars in the sky can be observed, described, predicted, and explained with models.

ESS1.B. This model of the solar system can explain eclipses of the sun and the moon. Earth's spin axis is fixed in direction over the short term but tilted relative to its orbit around the sun. The seasons are a result of that tilt and are caused by the differential intensity of sunlight on different areas of Earth across the year.

1. The Seasons

How do the seasons change where you live? You might have experienced a hot summer and a cold winter. Every year, you experience different seasons as the weather changes.

You also may have noticed that these changes follow a pattern. A pattern is something that happens in a regular and repeated way. Every year, you experience a pattern of temperature changes as Earth revolves around the sun.

How you experience seasons depends on where you are on Earth. Much of the United States, such as New York and Alaska, has cold winters and hot summers. Areas around the world at similar latitudes share this pattern. But Alaska's summers, though still warmer than its winters, are not as hot as New York's. Alaska and other places at or near Earth's poles tend to become very cold in the winter and remain somewhat cool in the summer. Hawaii, on the other hand, does not have as much variation in temperature because it is closer to the equator.

In Chicago, Illinois, summers are hot, and the winters are cold and snowy. You can observe seasonal patterns in Chicago over the course of a year.

The times of the year that you experience the seasons also depends on your location on Earth. In the Northern Hemisphere, December, January, and February are winter months, and June, July, and August are summer months. But in the Southern Hemisphere, the seasons are opposite! December is the start of summer, and June is the start of winter.

Another difference between the seasons is how long the sun is visible in the sky. In the winter, days are shorter because the sun is not in the sky for as long. The sun rises later in the morning and sets earlier in the evening. In the summer, the reverse is true. The sun is in the sky for a longer time because the sun rises earlier and sets later.

The timing of sunrise and sunset is not the only difference in the sun's apparent motion. Where the sun rises and sets changes with the seasons. In the Northern Hemisphere, the sun rises and sets farther south in the winter than it does in the summer. In the Southern Hemisphere, the sun rises and sets farther north in the winter than it does in the summer.

What causes the seasons to be so different? All the differences in the seasons, including changes in temperature, sunrise, and sunset, are caused by changes in the position of Earth's axis relative to the sun.

2. Earth's Shape and the Sun's Energy

If you go outside on a bright, cloudless day, you will feel the warmth of the sunlight on your skin. The sunlight that warms you also carries energy that warms Earth. But the light does not strike all parts of Earth in the same way. Why is it colder at the North and South Poles and warmer at the equator?

Uneven Heating and the Angle of the Sun's Light The angle at which sunlight strikes Earth determines how concentrated the light is. How concentrated the light is determines how much a spot on Earth is heated. As a result, some locations on Earth are always colder than other locations.

You can see how the angle that light strikes a surface affects the concentration of the light using a flashlight and a piece of paper. Suppose you hold the paper perpendicular to the flashlight. You would see the paper and the flashlight make a 90° angle, or a right angle. The light from the flashlight would form a circle on the paper. You can observe the circle that forms in Paper B of Figure 2.2A. But if you tilt the paper away from the flashlight, the light will form an oval on the paper. You can see that the oval is larger than the original circle.

The flashlight gives off the same amount of light no matter how the paper is oriented. When the paper is tilted, the light is spread out over a larger area. Each point in the oval of light receives less light than each point in the circle of light. When the paper is perpendicular, the light is more concentrated. When the light hits the paper, it transfers energy to the paper. More concentrated light transfers more energy to the paper.

Similarly, sunlight is more concentrated when it hits the Earth perpendicularly than when it hits it at a larger angle. Like the flashlight and paper, sunlight transfers more energy when it strikes Earth's surface perpendicularly than when it strikes the surface at a larger angle. When sunlight transfers more energy to the surface of Earth, it is heated more.

Figure 2.2A

When a flashlight shines on a perpendicular sheet of paper, the light forms a circle on the paper. When a flashlight shines on a tilted sheet of paper, the light forms a larger oval. The light in the circle is more concentrated than the light in the oval because it is not spread out as much.

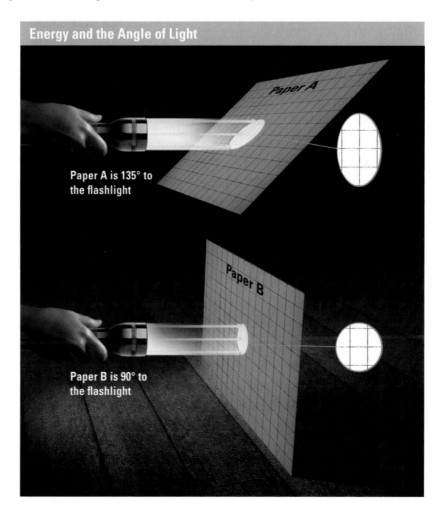

Energy and the Angle of Light

Paper A is 135° to the flashlight

Paper B is 90° to the flashlight

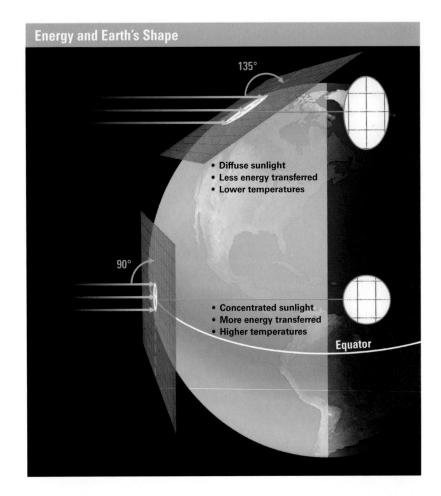

135°

- Diffuse sunlight
- Less energy transferred
- Lower temperatures

90°

- Concentrated sunlight
- More energy transferred
- Higher temperatures

Equator

Figure 2.2B

Since Earth is a sphere, sunlight strikes various parts of Earth at different angles. Near the equator, sunlight strikes Earth nearly perpendicularly and transfers a lot of energy to that part of Earth's surface. North of the equator, sunlight strikes at a larger angle, and less energy is transferred to that part of Earth's surface.

Earth's Shape and the Angle of the Sun's Light How does Earth's shape affect the angle that sunlight hits its surface? Earth is a sphere, so it does not have a flat surface. Therefore, sunlight always hits different parts of Earth at different angles.

You can model this by shining a flashlight on a large ball. If you point the flashlight at the center of the ball, the light mostly hits the ball perpendicularly to the ball's surface. You will see a circle of light on the ball similar to the circle on the perpendicular sheet of paper. But if you hold the flashlight so that it shines on the top half of the ball, the light hits the ball at an angle larger than a right angle. You will see an oval similar to the oval on the tilted sheet of paper. Just like the oval on the tilted paper, the oval on the ball covers a larger area than the circle.

The flashlight gives off the same amount of light regardless of which part of the ball it is shining on. But the light is spread out over a larger area when the light hits the ball at a larger angle than when it hits the ball perpendicularly. So, each point in the oval of light receives less energy from the flashlight than each point in the circle of light does.

Sunlight hits Earth in a similar way to how a flashlight strikes the surface of a ball. Near the equator, sunlight hits Earth's surface nearly perpendicularly. It transfers a large amount of energy to each spot on Earth's surface there. As a result, the climate near the equator at sea level is warm throughout the year.

At latitudes both north and south of the equator, light hits Earth's surface at a non-perpendicular angle. At these latitudes, the sunlight is more diffuse, and less energy is transferred to each spot on Earth's surface. The same amount of incoming energy is spread over a larger and larger area the farther away you move from the equator. The farther north or south you go, the colder the climate tends to be.

Earth's shape affects the angle that sunlight hits Earth's surface. The angle sunlight hits Earth's surface affects the amount of energy transferred to different parts of Earth. Because different amounts of energy are transferred to different parts of Earth, different locations are warmer or colder throughout the year.

3. Earth's Tilted Axis and the Seasons

Chicago experiences long days and warm weather during the summer. In the winter, it experiences snow and cold weather. During the summer, Chicago receives more energy due to the concentrated sunlight. However, during the winter, Chicago receives less energy from the sun. Chicago does not change location throughout the year, so why is sunlight more concentrated during different times of the year?

Different latitudes receive different amounts of sunlight throughout the year because Earth's axis is not perpendicular to its orbital plane. Earth's axis is tilted about 23.5°, so the North Pole appears to point to the same place in space throughout the year. This does not change as Earth revolves around the sun. Figure 2.3 models how Earth's axis remains tilted over the course of Earth's orbit in the Earth-sun system. A **system** is a set of connected parts that form a complex whole.

During parts of the year, the North Pole is tilted toward the sun. During this time, the northern latitudes receive more direct sunlight. The Northern Hemisphere is hotter and experiences summer. As Earth revolves, the northern latitudes receive less and less direct sunlight. They receive less and less energy, and start to cool down. During this part of the year, the Northern Hemisphere experiences autumn. Halfway through Earth's orbit, the North Pole is tilted away from the sun, so the northern latitudes receive less direct sunlight and experiences winter. Finally, as Earth continues on its orbit, the northern latitudes begin to receive more and more sunlight, and spring begins. Earth's tilted axis results in the seasons because latitudes receive different amounts of energy from the sun throughout the year as Earth revolves.

Figure 2.3

Earth rotates around an axis and revolves in an orbital plane. Earth's axis is not perpendicular to the orbital plane; instead it is tilted down 23.5°. This results in seasons since different latitudes receive more or less sunlight as Earth revolves around the sun over the course of a year.

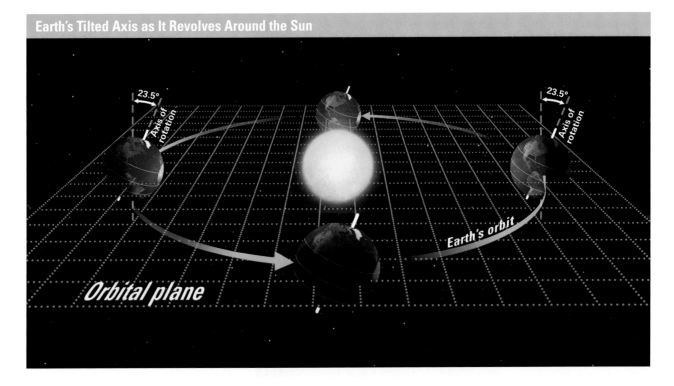

Earth's Tilted Axis as It Revolves Around the Sun

4. The Solstices

Throughout the year, Chicago receives more energy when the North Pole is tilted towards the sun and less energy when the North Pole is tilted away from the sun. Though Chicago never experiences direct sunlight, or sunlight at a 90° angle, it receives the most sunlight during a certain time of the year. On what day does this occur?

Chicago receives the most energy from the sun during the year on a day called the June Solstice. A **solstice** is a time of the year when the North or South Pole is closest to the sun during noon. During a solstice, the sun directly hits one of the tropics. The **tropics** are the latitudes furthest north and south that receive direct sunlight. The northern tropic is the Tropic of Cancer, located at 23.5°N, and the southern tropic is the Tropic of Capricorn, located at 23.5°S.

The June Solstice When the North Pole is tilted toward the sun, sunlight hits the Tropic of Cancer in the Northern Hemisphere at 90°. The day that sunlight hits the Topic of Cancer perpendicularly is called the June Solstice. The June Solstice is the day of the year that the Northern Hemisphere receives the most energy from the sun, and the Southern Hemisphere experiences the least. The June Solstice marks the first day of summer for the Northern Hemisphere, and the first day of winter for the Southern Hemisphere.

The December Solstice When Earth is on the other side of the sun, the Tropic of Capricorn in the Southern Hemisphere receives the most energy from the sun. This is the December Solstice, when Earth's South Pole is closest to the sun. The December Solstice is the day of the year where the Southern Hemisphere receives the most energy and the Northern Hemisphere receives the least energy from the sun. The December Solstice marks the first day of winter for the Northern Hemisphere, and the first day of summer for the Southern Hemisphere.

Figure 2.4

Because Earth is a sphere, the angle that sunlight hits the surface changes as you move north or south. This change in angle changes which latitude receives the most direct sunlight. During the solstices, the tropics receive the most light from the sun.

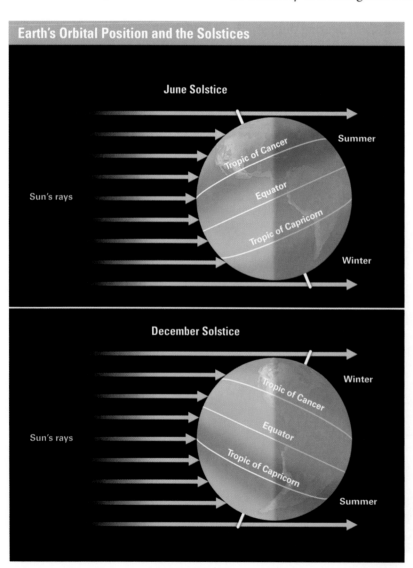

Earth's Orbital Position and the Solstices

June Solstice

Sun's rays

Tropic of Cancer

Equator

Tropic of Capricorn

Summer

Winter

December Solstice

Sun's rays

Tropic of Cancer

Equator

Tropic of Capricorn

Winter

Summer

5. The Equinoxes

During the June Solstice, Chicago receives the most sunlight it will during the year. This is true for most places in the Northern Hemisphere. But what about places on Earth's equator? They receive the same amount of sunlight on the June Solstice as they do on the December Solstice. When do they receive the most sunlight?

When the North and South Pole are an equal distance from the sun, the latitude that receives the most energy from the sun is 0 latitude, or the equator. An **equinox** is a time of the year when the sun is directly overhead at the equator during noon. During an equinox, places on the equator experience sunlight at a 90° angle. When do the equinoxes occur?

The September Equinox After the June Solstice, Earth continues to revolve around the sun. Earth's axis remains tilted, pointing towards the same place in space. Earth travels on its orbit until it is halfway between the solstices. As it travels, different latitudes receive more light from the sun. The latitudes closer to the equator receive more and more concentrated sunlight until the equator, or 0 latitude, receives sunlight at a perpendicular angle. This is the September Equinox. The September Equinox marks the first day of autumn in the Northern Hemisphere, and the first day of spring in the Southern Hemisphere.

The March Equinox After the December Solstice, when the Tropic of Capricorn at 23.5°S experiences its longest day of the year, Earth continues to revolve until the North and South Poles are once again equal distance from the sun. This is the March Equinox. Like the September Equinox, places on the equator receive the most energy from the sun during the March Equinox. The March Equinox marks the first day of spring for the Northern Hemisphere, and the first day of autumn for the Southern Hemisphere.

Figure 2.5

When the North and South Poles are equal distance from the sun, Earth experiences an equinox. During an equinox, the equator receives sunlight at a perpendicular angle.

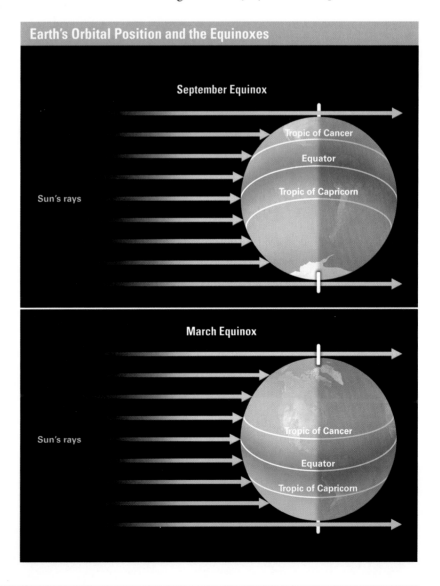

Earth's Orbital Position and the Equinoxes

September Equinox

Tropic of Cancer

Equator

Tropic of Capricorn

Sun's rays

March Equinox

Tropic of Cancer

Equator

Tropic of Capricorn

Sun's rays

The Sun's Energy and the Seasons

Earth and the sun work as parts of a system to produce seasons on Earth. Earth's round surface results in warmer climates at the equator and colder climates near the poles. Earth's tilted axis causes different latitudes to receive more or less concentrated sunlight during different points of a year. So, Jared in Denver, Colorado, and Marta in Buenos Aires, Argentina, experience different seasons over a year.

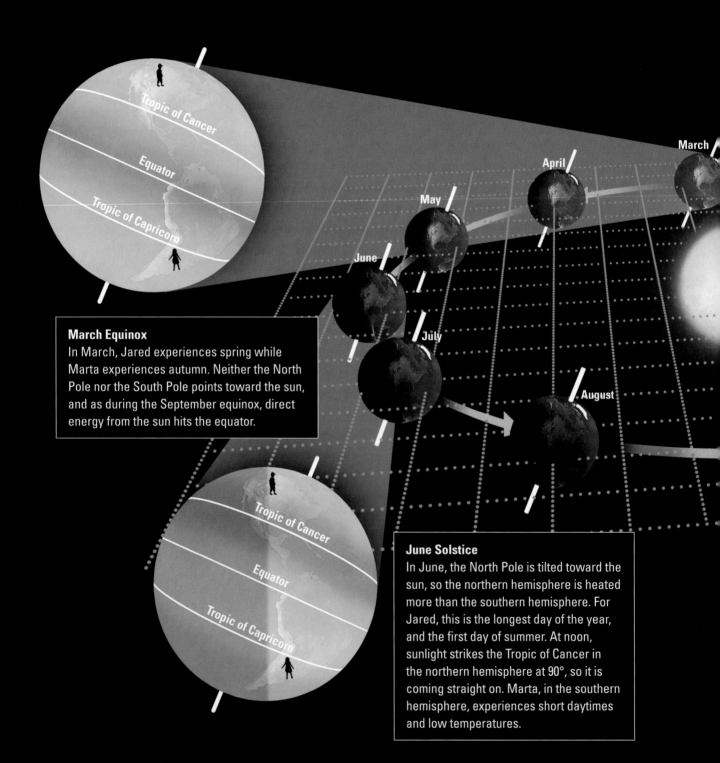

March Equinox

In March, Jared experiences spring while Marta experiences autumn. Neither the North Pole nor the South Pole points toward the sun, and as during the September equinox, direct energy from the sun hits the equator.

June Solstice

In June, the North Pole is tilted toward the sun, so the northern hemisphere is heated more than the southern hemisphere. For Jared, this is the longest day of the year, and the first day of summer. At noon, sunlight strikes the Tropic of Cancer in the northern hemisphere at 90°, so it is coming straight on. Marta, in the southern hemisphere, experiences short daytimes and low temperatures.

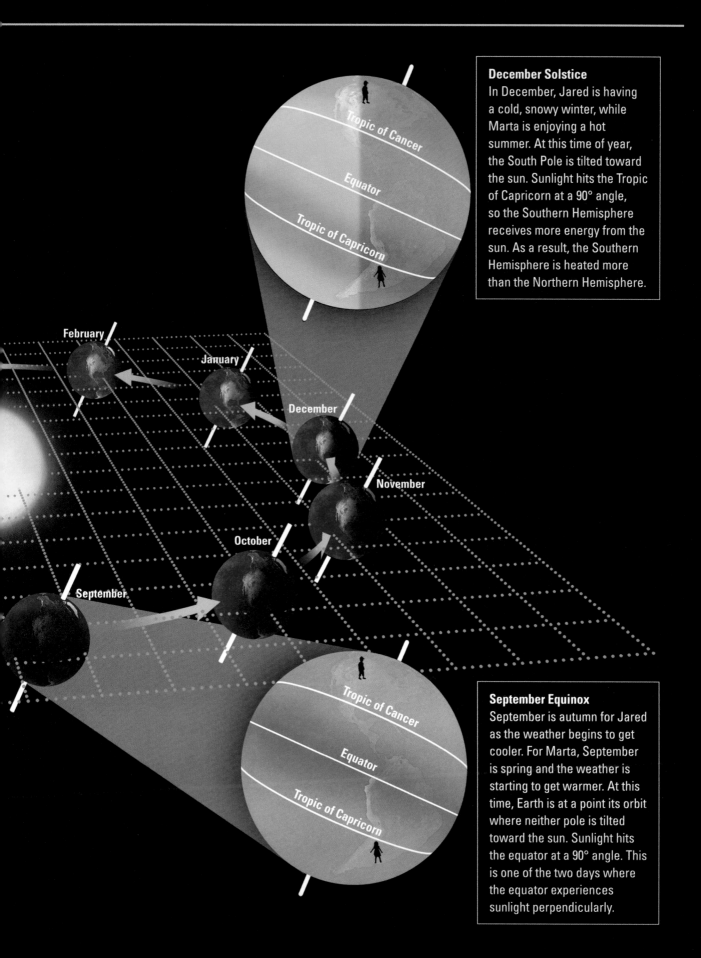

December Solstice

In December, Jared is having a cold, snowy winter, while Marta is enjoying a hot summer. At this time of year, the South Pole is tilted toward the sun. Sunlight hits the Tropic of Capricorn at a 90° angle, so the Southern Hemisphere receives more energy from the sun. As a result, the Southern Hemisphere is heated more than the Northern Hemisphere.

September Equinox

September is autumn for Jared as the weather begins to get cooler. For Marta, September is spring and the weather is starting to get warmer. At this time, Earth is at a point its orbit where neither pole is tilted toward the sun. Sunlight hits the equator at a 90° angle. This is one of the two days where the equator experiences sunlight perpendicularly.

The path of the sun in the sky changes throughout the year. This photo shows the path of the sun in Rochester, New York, every day from December of one year to June in the next. The highest path was traced in June and the lowest path was traced in December.

6. The Seasons and the Sun's Path in the Sky

Have you ever noticed that the sun shines longer on summer days when you don't have school? It is not your imagination! The sun does stay in the sky longer in the summer.

A change in temperature is not the only difference between the seasons. The length of the day and where the sun rises and sets also changes with the seasons. This is why your family can have a picnic dinner in the park after 7 P.M. in bright sunlight!

The height of the sun and amount of time the sun is visible in the sky each day changes throughout the year. In June in Chicago, the sun travels a path that arcs high in the sky, and remains there for about 15 hours. In December, the sun does not rise as high above the horizon and remains in the sky for only a little more than 9 hours. What causes this seasonal change? The height of the sun that you observe from Earth is related to the angle that sunlight strikes Earth's surface. The sun travels higher and is visible for longer when sunlight hits Earth's surface at a perpendicular angle. When sunlight hits Earth's surface at a non-perpendicular angle, the sun travels a path that arcs lower in the sky. Both of these effects are caused by the tilt of Earth's axis relative to the sun.

The location of sunrise and sunset also changes with the seasons. People usually say that the sun rises in the east and sets in the west. But for most places on Earth, the sun does not rise exactly in the east and set exactly in the west. Instead, in the Northern Hemisphere, the sun rises toward the southeast in the winter and toward the northeast in the summer.

7. Calendars of Ancient Civilizations

Spring, summer, autumn and winter all begin on an equinox or a solstice. If you wanted to look up the first day of spring, you could check a calendar or search online. However, ancient civilizations did not have the tools we do now. How did they know which day the equinox or the solstice would occur?

Ancient people also used calendars to determine the start of each season. But their calendars were unlike calendars you might use today. Ancient civilizations built large structures that tracked the motion of the sun. The alignment of rocks at Stonehenge frame the sun at sunrise on the June solstice and at sunset on the December solstice. Though there are no records from the people who built Stonehenge, some people speculate that the rocks were placed there deliberately and adjusted until they were at this position.

Stonehenge shows that ancient civilizations knew that the seasons were related to the sun and its path in the sky. But they did not know that it is the tilt of Earth's axis and Earth's orbit around the sun that causes the change of seasons.

The alignment of the rocks at Stonehenge frame the sun at sunrise on the June solstice. Though there are no records, some people believe the rocks were placed there deliberately to mark the seasons.

LESSON SUMMARY

Earth's Tilted Axis

The Seasons Each year, Earth experiences changes in temperature, length of daytime, and location of sunrise and sunset. These changes occur in a yearly pattern, which are called seasons.

Earth's Shape and the Sun's Energy Earth is unevenly heated by the sun because Earth's shape causes sunlight to hit Earth's surface at different angles. When the angle is perpendicular, light is more concentrated.

Earth's Tilted Axis and the Seasons Earth's axis is not perpendicular to its orbital plane. Instead, the axis is tilted approximately 23.5°. As Earth revolves around the sun, different latitudes receive more energy from the sun and seasons occur.

The Solstices A solstice is the time when the North or South Pole is closest to the sun. During the solstice, the Tropic of Capricorn or Tropic of Cancer receives the most light and energy from the sun.

The Equinoxes An equinox is a day where the North and South Pole are an equal distance from the sun. During the equinoxes, the equator receives the most light and energy from the sun.

The Seasons and the Sun's Path in the Sky Other seasonal patterns include the height of the sun, length of daytime, and where the sun rises and sets.

Calendars of Ancient Civilizations Ancient people monitored the seasons by building structures that tracked the motion of the sun.

Capturing the Sun's Path

Imagine doing an art project that takes months to complete, and you can't look at it the entire time you are working on it. The images shown are examples of such a project. How were they made, and why did they take so long to make?

The images you see here are solargraphs. A solargraph is a long term exposure of the sky taken with a pinhole camera. In photography, an *exposure* is the process of allowing light to hit a light-sensitive surface. In a pinhole camera used to take solargraphs, the light-sensitive surface is a piece of paper treated with a substance that changes color when light shines on it.

A solargraph shows the sun's path over several days or several months, and each bright line in a solargraph is the path of the sun for one day. Recall that the position and length of the sun's path depends on the time of the year. In most places in the world, the sun traces a higher arc in the sky in the summer, and it traces a lower arc in the winter. Therefore, the sun takes a slightly different path in the sky every day.

The solargraphs shown here were taken in the same way, but they look different. The differences are the result of four factors. First, the location where a solargraph is taken affects the shape and height of the sun tracks. When it is taken also matters. The length of the exposure affects the number of tracks recorded, and the direction that the camera is pointed affects what part of the sky is seen.

These four solargraphs are very different because they were taken in different places and at different times of the year. They also look different because of the lengths of the exposures and the direction the cameras were pointed.

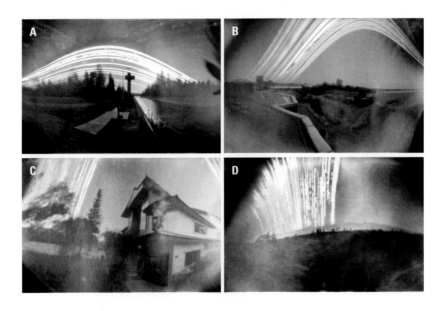

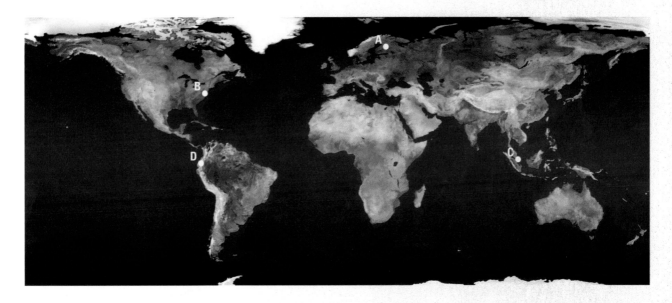

Solargraph A was taken in Varkaus, Finland, which is at 62°N latitude, near the Arctic Circle. The sun tracks in the solargraph are low because it was taken at a relatively high latitude. The solargraph was taken in fall and winter, so the sun followed arcs that did not rise high above the horizon. The exposure time was three months, so about 90 sun tracks were recorded.

Solargraph B was taken in Baltimore, Maryland, which is at 39°N latitude. One reason the sun tracks in Solargraph B arc higher than the ones in Solargraph A is because of the latitude where it was taken. Baltimore has a lower latitude than Varkaus, so the sun follows a higher path in the sky. The tracks are higher also because Solargraph B was taken in the summer.

Solargraph C was taken in Singapore, which is at 1°N latitude. Because Singapore is very close to the equator, the sun travels very high in the sky all year long, and as a result, the top of the sun's arcs did not fit in this solargraph. The sun moved out of the pinhole camera's frame every day.

Solargraph D was taken in Quito, Ecuador, which is located on Earth's equator. The latitude of this solargraph is similar to the latitude of Solargraph C, but the two look different because of the directions that the pinhole cameras were pointed. The camera that took Solargraph C was pointed to the north or the south, so you can see the east and west sides of the sun's tracks; the camera that took Solargraph D was pointed to either the east or the west.

Although you can see only one end of the sun's tracks in Solargraph D, you can see that the sun did follow different paths. The tracks on the right are nearly vertical, which shows that the sun moved directly overhead on those days. The tracks on the left angle slightly, which shows that the sun did not rise as high on those days.

The map shows where Solargraphs A, B, C, and D were taken. One reason the solargraphs look different is because they were taken in different locations.

Artist Tarja Trygg planned and carried out a project to collect solargraphs from around the world and share them with people everywhere. By the end of her project, she had more than 350 solargraphs on display.

Making a Pinhole Camera

The solargraphs you've seen were collected as part of a project by a Finnish art student named Tarja Trygg. In her project, Trygg collected solargraphs from all over the world and matched them to their locations on a world map. But Trygg could not travel throughout the world setting up pinhole cameras, so she set up a website and invited people to contribute to her project. The website included instructions on how to construct a pinhole camera. Eventually, hundreds of people sent her the solargraphs taken from places all over the world.

You can also make a pinhole camera and create solargraphs. A pinhole camera is simple to make using easily obtained supplies. First, with an adult, cut the top off a tall aluminum beverage can with a can opener. Make sure the can is clean and dry, and be careful not to touch the sharp, newly cut edge. Then, use black cardstock and waterproof duct tape to create a lid for the can, making sure that the lid is snug so no light will get in. But (for now) it should not be taped onto the can. Only use the duct tape to hold the cardstock in a lid-shape, and cover the cardstock with duct tape to make it waterproof.

Use a straight sewing pin to poke a hole in the side of the can about 8 cm from the bottom of the can. The pinhole is your camera's aperture, or opening, which will project an image on the light-sensitive paper that you will put inside. Cover the pinhole with a small piece of duct tape, which will be your camera's shutter. It will keep the lens closed until you are ready to expose the paper to light.

In a dimly lit room, remove the lid that you made and put a piece of 5×7-inch, black-and-white photographic paper in the can. The paper should be placed so that it does not cover the pinhole and so that the light-sensitive side is facing inside. Put the lid back on the can, and use more duct tape to secure the lid to the can, making sure that the piece of tape does not cover the pinhole.

Each pinhole camera takes one solargraph. To take a solargraph, remove the duct-tape shutter to open the camera's aperture. The light-sensitive paper inside will be continually exposed throughout the time that the aperture is open.

If you were to take a solargraph, where would you put the camera? What factors do you think would influence the images captured?

Using a Pinhole Camera

Place the camera outside with the pinhole facing south if you are in the Northern Hemisphere or facing north if you are in the Southern Hemisphere. The camera should be placed in an area that has a relatively clear view of the sky, and it should be secured to something that will not move. A lamp post, a tree, or the window ledge of a building are all good things to attach the camera to.

Once the camera is in place, remove the piece of tape covering the pinhole to begin your exposure. Leave the camera in place for at least two weeks, but remember that the longer you leave it, the more sun tracks your solargraph will record.

When you are ready look at your solargraph, use a new piece of duct tape to cover the pinhole before you move your camera. Take the whole camera home or to school, and in a dimly lit room, carefully remove the lid and use a hair dryer to dry any moisture that collected in the can. Take the photographic paper from the can and scan it in color on a flatbed scanner. The scan is a negative image, so the sun tracks will look dark in the scan. Use photo-processing software to "invert" the colors, which will turn the negative image into a positive image; the positive image is your solargraph.

Tarja Trygg is no longer collecting solargraphs for her art project, but that does not mean you cannot make one for yourself. Make a pinhole camera, set it up, and NO PEEKING! If you're patient, you should be rewarded with your own amazing image in a few weeks. ◆

A pinhole camera for taking solargraphs can be constructed using easily found materials. The "film" for the camera is light-sensitive photographic paper, which can be bought online or at a specialty camera store.

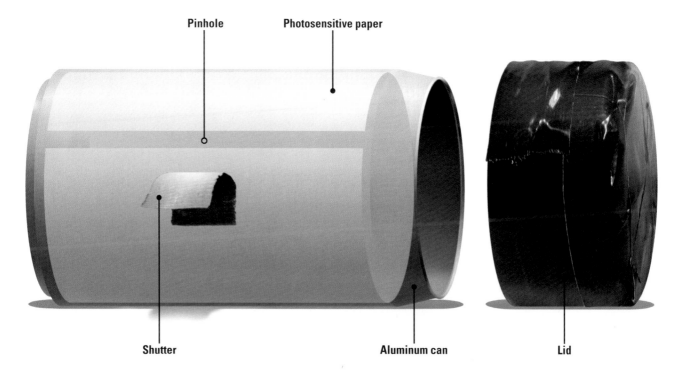

Pinhole **Photosensitive paper**

Shutter **Aluminum can** **Lid**

Phases of the Moon

Why does the moon seem to change shape?

Introduction

As you look towards the big round moon, it sets toward the west as the sun rises toward the east, behind you. The trees glow orange in the early morning light, and the purple sky on the horizon is the last of the night sky disappearing from sight.

You know that the round moon in the photo is called a *full moon*. You probably also have observed that the moon appears to have different shapes on different nights. These shapes, or lunar phases, follow a distinct repeating pattern. How can understanding this pattern help you understand the causes of lunar phases?

The Earth, sun, and moon are a system of moving parts that follow a pattern. In this lesson, you will explore how the arrangement of these celestial bodies in this system changes. You will learn how the moon lights up and how the relative positions of the sun, the moon, and Earth change to cause lunar phases. The explanation for this pattern also explains a pattern in moonrises and moonsets.

Throughout the lesson, you will use different models to understand moon phases: physical models using objects, graphic models such as diagrams, and conceptual models that you can think about. These models will demonstrate how the positions of the sun, the moon, and Earth affect what you observe from Earth's surface.

Lunar phases in this lesson are described from the perspective of the Northern Hemisphere. In the Northern Hemisphere, the moon appears to grow from the right and shrink from the left. In the Southern Hemisphere, the moon appears to grow from the left and shrink from the right.

Vocabulary

model a representation which displays some but not all aspects of an object or phenomenon

lunar phase the appearance of the lit area of the moon as seen from Earth

new moon the lunar phase where the moon is directly between Earth and the sun; the new moon cannot be seen from Earth

first quarter moon the lunar phase where the moon, Earth, and the sun form a perpendicular angle; the moon looks like a semicircle with only the right half visible

third quarter moon the lunar phase where the moon, Earth, and the sun form a perpendicular angle; the moon looks like a semicircle with only the left half visible

full moon the lunar phase where Earth is directly between the sun and the moon; the moon looks like a circle

---

Next Generation Science Standards

Performance Expectations
MS-ESS1-1. Develop and use a model of the Earth-sun-moon system to describe the cyclic patterns of lunar phases, eclipses of the sun and moon, and seasons.

MS-ETS1-1. Define the criteria and constraints of a design problem with sufficient precision to ensure a successful solution, taking into account relevant scientific principles and potential impacts on people and the natural environment that may limit possible solutions.

Science and Engineering Practices
Developing and Using Models Develop and use a model to describe phenomena.

Asking Questions and Defining Problems Define a design problem that can be solved through the development of an object, tool, process or system and includes multiple criteria and constraints, including scientific knowledge that may limit possible solutions.

Crosscutting Concepts
Patterns Patterns can be used to identify cause and effect relationships.

Disciplinary Core Ideas
ESS1.A. Patterns of the apparent motion of the sun, the moon, and stars in the sky can be observed, described, predicted, and explained with models.

ETS1.A. The more precisely a design task's criteria and constraints can be defined, the more likely it is that the designed solution will be successful. Specification of constraints includes consideration of scientific principles and other relevant knowledge that are likely to limit possible solutions.

Unlike most celestial objects, the moon appears to change shape every day. The moon also appears in the sky at various times. Sometimes, the moon is in the sky during the day. Other times, the moon is only in the sky at night.

1. The Changing Moon

People throughout history observed the moon's changing patterns. Many ancient cultures and astronomers told myths to explain these changes. You know that the moon is a sphere-shaped celestial body in space. Yet sometimes it looks round, and at other times it looks like a peach with a big bite taken out of it. What patterns can you observe about the moon?

The moon seems to change shape from one day to the next in a particular pattern. Suppose you saw the moon as a complete circle on one night. The next night, it appears as not quite a full circle; it will look like a circle with one edge cut off. Then the following night, even more of the circle will seem to have disappeared. If you kept observing the moon's shape for about a month, you would see it change from a *full moon* (a full circle) to a crescent shape to a backwards-crescent shape and then back to a full moon.

From Earth, the moon appears to be different from most other celestial objects. The moon's changing shape and varied rising and setting times are two patterns that most other celestial objects do not appear to have. Over the years, scientists have come up with scientific theories to explain how these patterns can occur, given that the moon is a sphere.

2. The Sun Lights Up the Moon

How can a sphere appear to change shape over a month? A peach appears to change shape as you take bites out of it, but the moon is not being eaten over the course of a month. How can you study the moon to understand its changing patterns?

Scientists use models to help understand far away objects such as the sun or the moon. A **model** is a representation of an object or phenomenon, which makes important aspects easier to observe and simplifies less important aspects. You can model how the sun appears by using a bare light bulb standing in the middle of a dark room. No matter where you stand in relationship to this spherical bulb, it will always appear as a circle.

Models can also explain how the moon is illuminated, or lit up. The moon is a sphere, too, but it does not produce visible light of its own. You see the moon because the sun shines on the moon. Sunlight hits the moon and reflects off of it similar to how light reflects off of a mirror. When the reflected light reaches your eyes, you see the lit-up part of the moon. This is similar to turning on a bare light bulb in a dark room. When you go into a dark room, you cannot see any objects that might be there. However, when you turn on the light, objects become illuminated. When the light from the light bulb hits an object, such as a ball, some light reflects off it. You see the ball when the reflected light reaches your eyes.

At any moment, the sun shines on half of the moon. As you can see in Figure 3.2, the other half of the moon is dark. From Earth, you can see the part of the moon that the sun shines on. What we see from Earth depends on what part of the moon is being illuminated.

Figure 3.2

The moon does not produce its own visible light. Light from the sun hits the moon and reflects off it. From Earth, we can sometimes see the part of the moon that is illuminated by the sun.

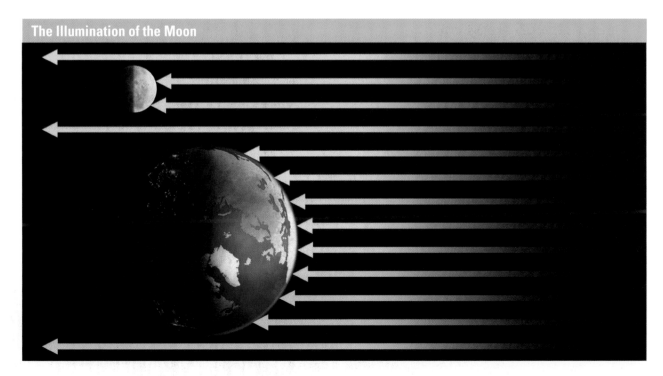

The Illumination of the Moon

3. Modeling the Earth-Sun-Moon System

When you shine a light bulb on a ball in a dark room, the light shines on half the ball. If you are standing in the right place, the ball appears as a circle. But the moon does not always appear as a circle! Instead, it changes in a pattern. How can you explain this phenomenon?

You can explain how the moon changes in a pattern using models. Suppose you were standing in the dark room with a bare light bulb behind you. You hold a ball in front of you, and you can see all of the lit half of the ball, which looks like a circle. Keeping your arm straight in front of you, you rotate 90° to your left, and see the left side of the circle lit while the right side is dark. Half the ball is still lit up, but you can see only part of the lit area. As you continue to rotate, you see a different amount of the ball. In fact, you would see the shape change from a full circle to a crescent shape to a backwards crescent shape and then back to a full circle. You have just modeled how the moon changes over the course of a month, using a light bulb to represent the sun and a ball to represent the moon.

The relative positions of the celestial objects in the Earth-sun-moon system determine how the moon appears from Earth. The moon is visible when the sunlight hits its surface and reflects toward Earth, so the moon's position around Earth determines what part of the lit up moon you can see. For example, when the moon is not visible, the sun and the moon are on the same side of Earth. When the moon appears as a complete circle, the sun and the moon are on opposite sides of Earth.

People can model the moon phases because they occur due to consistent patterns. Scientists can use their models to make predictions about when moon phases will appear.

Scientists can use models, like this orrery, to represent how the moon appears to change as its position in the Earth-sun-moon system changes. As you rotate Earth around the sun, the moon rotates around Earth. Models help scientists understand concepts so that they can make predictions.

4. The Earth-Sun-Moon System

You set up a camera to record the sky for a whole month. Each day, the moon changes shape, growing from an empty space into a crescent, a half-circle, and then a round circle. Eventually, it shrinks back down into a half-circle and then a crescent before disappearing from the sky again. How can we describe each shape?

Recall that only the sunlit part of the moon is visible from Earth. As the moon orbits around Earth, different parts of the moon are lit up by the sun. The moon appears to change shape because people see different amounts of the lit part of the moon. The different shapes are called lunar phases. A **lunar phase** is the shape of the lit area of the moon as seen from Earth.

The Pattern of the Phases The lunar phases, shown in Figure 3.4A, always follow the same pattern. During a **new moon,** the moon is directly between Earth and the sun. None of the lit side of the moon faces Earth, so the moon cannot be seen from Earth. About seven days later, the moon is one quarter of the way through its revolution around Earth. This lunar phase is a **first quarter moon,** where the moon, Earth, and the sun form a perpendicular angle. During a first quarter moon, the moon looks like a semicircle with only the right half visible.

Figure 3.4A
The lunar phases change in a regular pattern. The new moon grows, or waxes, until it becomes a first quarter moon. It continues to wax until it appears as a full moon. Then, it shrinks, or wanes, until it becomes a third quarter moon and a new moon.

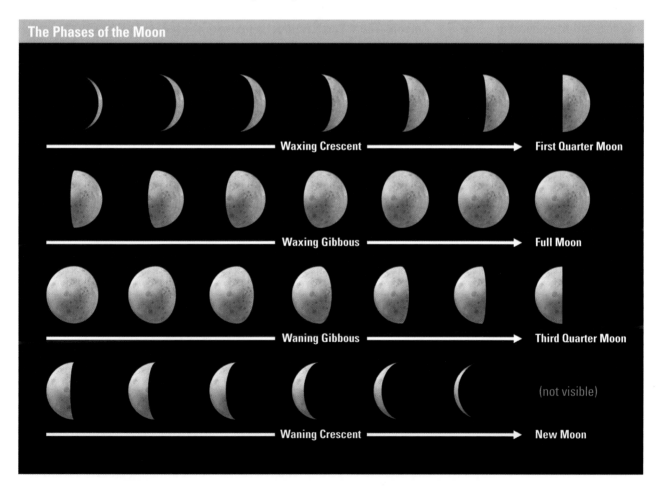

The Phases of the Moon

Waxing Crescent ⟶ First Quarter Moon

Waxing Gibbous ⟶ Full Moon

Waning Gibbous ⟶ Third Quarter Moon

Waning Crescent ⟶ New Moon

(not visible)

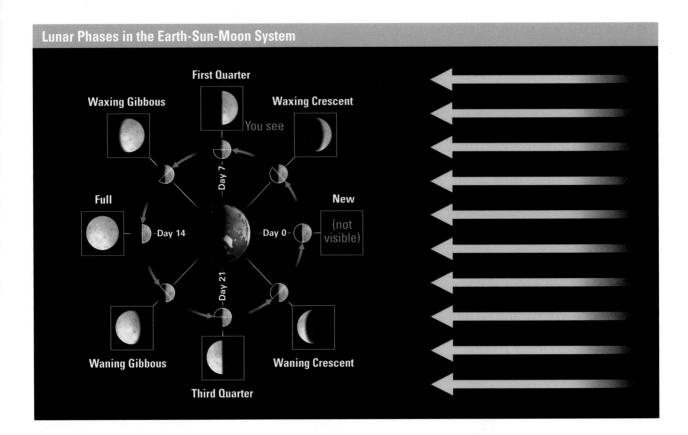

Figure 3.4B

This diagram shows how the arrangement of Earth, the sun, and the moon determines the lunar phase, though the distances between Earth and the moon are not accurate. For example, the sun and the moon are on the same side of Earth during a new moon and are on opposite sides of Earth during a full moon.

About seven days after the first quarter moon, the moon is a **full moon,** where Earth is directly between the moon and the sun. The full moon phase looks like a complete circle. After about another seven days, the moon is three-quarters of the way through its revolution around Earth. This lunar phase is a **third quarter moon** (or last quarter moon), where the sun, Earth, and the moon form a perpendicular angle. During a third quarter moon, the moon looks like a semicircle with the left-half side visible. About seven days later, the moon will complete its revolution and appear as a new moon again.

The Other Names of the Phases The full moon, the new moon, and the quarter moons are the four main lunar phases. Other phases fit in between the four main phases and are named after their shapes and how the moon appears to be growing or shrinking.

When the moon's shape is larger than a semicircle, but not a full circle, it is a *gibbous moon*. When the moon's shape is smaller than a semicircle, but not completely dark, it is a *crescent moon*. When the moon is going from a new moon to a full moon, the moon appears to be growing, or *waxing*. When the moon is going from a full moon to a new moon, the moon appears to be shrinking, or *waning*.

To name the phases between the four main phases, you combine *waxing* or *waning* with *gibbous* or *crescent*. The phase between a full moon and a third quarter moon has a gibbous shape, and the moon appears to be getting smaller, so it is called a *waning gibbous moon*.

Moon Phases and the Earth-Sun-Moon System

The sun shines on the side of the moon that faces the sun. People on Earth see only the part of the moon that is lit. However, the amount of the lit moon that can be seen changes as the moon revolves around Earth. Though the distances and sizes in this diagram are not to scale, it depicts the cause and effect relationships between the arrangement of Earth, the sun, and the moon, and the lunar phases observed from Earth.

not visible	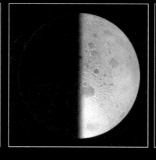		
New Moon	**First Quarter Moon**	**Full Moon**	**Third Quarter Moon**
When the moon is on the same side of Earth as the sun is, you cannot see any of the lit half of the moon because that half is pointed away from Earth. The moon is in the new moon phase and cannot be seen from Earth.	When the moon is a quarter of the way around its orbit around Earth, you can see half of the lit part of the moon. The moon looks like the right half of circle and is in the first quarter phase.	When the moon is on the opposite side of Earth from the sun, you can see all the lit half of the moon. The moon looks like a circle and is a full moon.	When the moon is three-quarters of the way around its orbit, you can see half of the lit part of the moon again. But this time, you see the left half of the moon. The moon is a third quarter moon.

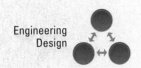

5. Reducing Risk for Apollo 11

On July 20, 1969, people around the world watched on live television as Commander Neil Armstrong stepped onto the surface of the moon. It was the first time a human walked on the surface of another celestial body. Knowing about relative positions of the moon, sun, and Earth was just one of the many scientific ideas the Apollo 11 team needed to make it possible.

With worldwide attention on this historic moment, scientists and engineers at NASA, the U.S. space agency, wanted to make sure the equipment and systems they designed all worked. Their two main criteria were that humans land on the moon and safely return to Earth. But these were not the only ones.

While designing the mission, the NASA team defined precise criteria and constraints for each of the many stages of the mission. One of the constraints was that the time of day they could successfully launch was limited to precisely a few hours a day. Only within this time period could a spacecraft launch from Florida and land on the site on the Moon chosen by the team. Also, the day of the month they could launch was limited to a few days during the lunar phase cycle.

Deciding where to land had its own long list of criteria and constraints. Among the criteria was that the astronauts had to land on a site near the moon's equator. This would use less fuel than landing far from the equator. Also, the landing site had to be smooth, with few craters and boulders. Nor could there be any hills or cliffs along the approach path.

The date and time to touch down was also important. Among the criteria was that the astronauts land during the waxing crescent phase of the moon. During this phase, it would be just after sunrise on the landing site. The team also determined that the landing time should be during a time period when sunlight struck the moon at an angle of no less than 5 degrees and no greater than 14 degrees. At these angles, the long shadows would make features of the lunar landscape clearly visible to the astronauts. It was a good thing that this criterion was met. During the actual descent, Commander Armstrong saw that they were about to land inside a large boulder-filled crater. He quickly took over the automatic landing controls and navigated to a safer landing area.

Landing humans on the moon and bringing them home safely were the overall criteria for the Apollo 11 mission. There were three American astronauts on the mission, and two walked on the lunar surface. This photo of "Buzz" Aldrin was captured by Commander Neil Armstrong.

Once the landing stage of the mission was completed, the astronauts had to be safely carried back to Earth. They carefully planned when and how long to fire their engines to put them on a course so that the gravitational force of Earth could pull them back home. A "free-return trajectory" was less risky than other options for getting the astronauts home. Using their carefully defined criteria, they fired their engines for 151 seconds to put them on the path to Earth. Since their execution was so precise, they only had to make one correction during the entire path home, firing their engine for 10 seconds to adjust their course.

The failure or success of the thousands of engineering solutions that went into the Apollo 11 mission would be on view for the entire world to see. The risks were great, but the team took great care in dealing with them. Reflecting on the efforts of the mission design team, Neil Armstrong said ". . . when you have hundreds of thousands of people all doing their job a little better than they have to, you get an improvement in performance. And that's the only reason we could have pulled this whole thing off."

Landing the first humans on the moon required many individual decisions. On July 24, 1969, engineers and scientists at Mission Control erupted in joyous celebration when the three Apollo 11 astronauts returned safely to Earth.

LESSON SUMMARY
Phases of the Moon

The Changing Moon When observing the sky with your eyes, the moon seems different from other celestial objects because it appears to change shape and can be found in the sky at various times.

The Sun Lights Up the Moon You see the moon because light from the sun shines on the moon and reflects to your eyes. The sun lights up only the half of the moon that faces the sun.

Modeling the Earth-Sun-Moon System The relative positions of the sun, the moon, and Earth change what part of the moon is visible from Earth.

The Earth-Sun-Moon System You see moon phases because of the relative position of the celestial bodies in the Earth-sun-moon system. As the moon revolves around Earth, the amount of the lit half of the moon you can see changes, producing the lunar phases seen from Earth. The four main lunar phases are a new moon, a first quarter moon, a full moon, and a third quarter (or last quarter) moon.

Reducing Risk for Apollo 11 Engineers used their understanding of the relative positions of celestial bodies in the Earth-sun-moon system to help them define precise criteria and constraints. They used this to land humans on the surface of the moon and bring them safely back to Earth.

The Changing Tides

These photos were taken at the Bay of Fundy on the Atlantic coast of Canada in the same place at two different times of the day. You may wonder: did a huge rainstorm flood the area? The water level change is not a result of rain or anything else on Earth. It is the result of tides caused by the moon. How does the moon, which is around 380,000 kilometers away from Earth, cause changes in water levels in bodies of water on Earth?

Picture you and your family vacationing here at the Bay of Fundy. The first morning, you go to the beach and explore around the giant rock formations. You leave the beach to have lunch and return to the same place later in the afternoon to join a kayak tour. The beach looks completely different because the bottoms of the rock formations seem to have disappeared!

You ask the tour leader what happened to the rocks, and she explains that the bottoms of the formations are underwater. She tells you that the Bay of Fundy is the place on Earth that has the greatest typical change in water level due to tides.

A *tide* is the periodic rise and fall of the water level in the ocean or other body of water. The ocean water levels change continually throughout each day, and two points in the cycle have special names. *High tide* happens when the water level is at its highest point, and *low tide* happens when the water level is at its lowest point. Tides are most clearly seen on coastlines. Usually, every point on an ocean coastline has two high tides and two low tides each day.

The water level in the Bay of Fundy changes dramatically throughout the day: from low tide (left) to high tide (right). This change in water level is due to tides.

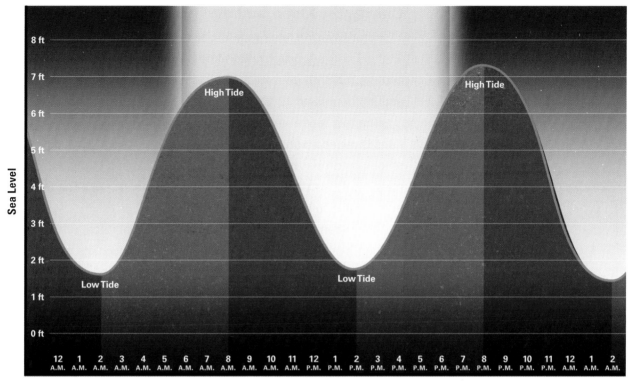

Time of Day

Timing the Tides

As you paddle along in the water, you might ask the tour leader how she knew that the bay would be at high tide when she took the group out. She explains that the times of high tide and low tide change from day to day, so she can use a tide chart to plan her tour schedule.

A tide chart shows how the tide changes at a point on the coastline. A tide chart is sometimes shown as a graph that has the time of day along the x-axis and the water height along the y-axis. On many a tide charts, the average water height at low tide is set at 0 meters, but actual water height at low tide can be above or below the 0-meter level.

You can use a tide chart to find the predicted time and height of each tide. A wavy line represents the water level in a tide chart—the higher the line, the higher the tide. To find the time when a high tide will happen, draw a line from the high points of the line to the x-axis. To find its height, draw a line from the top parts of the wavy line to the y-axis. You can follow a similar procedure to find the time and height of a low tide. You can also use a tide chart to find the water height at any time during the day. To do this, draw a line up from the time of day that you are interested in to the wavy line. The y-axis value of where your line meets the wavy line shows the water level at your chosen time.

A tide chart, such as the one shown here, is sometimes shown as a graph. The crests of the chart correspond to high tides, and the troughs correspond to low tides. High tide and low tide each happen twice a day. According to this tide chart, high tide happens at about 8 A.M. and 8 P.M., while low tide happens at just after 2 A.M. and again at almost 2 P.M.

Gravity, the Moon, and the Tides

After kayaking, your tour leader might show you a tide chart, and you notice a pattern. High tides and low tides always alternate, and the time between each high tide and each low tide is always about 6 hours and 12.5 minutes. Why does this pattern occur?

The tour leader explains: the even separation between the tides is caused by gravitational force, the rotation of Earth, and the revolution of the moon. Gravitational force causes the tides; the rotation of Earth and the revolution of the moon cause the tides to occur in a regular pattern.

The moon pulls on Earth with a gravitational force, which is strongest on the part of Earth closest to the moon. The stronger pull causes the water on the side of Earth facing the moon to flow upward into a bulge. This bulge causes the water level to rise on that side of Earth, forming a high tide.

Another bulge of water forms on the side of Earth farthest from the moon. This bulge forms because the moon pulls least on that side of Earth. It pulls more on the middle of Earth than it does on the far side. So, the moon pulls the middle of Earth away from the water on the far side, and the water flows into a bulge facing away from the moon as seen in the diagrams. This bulge forms a second high tide.

Halfway in between the bulges, the water levels are lower than in the bulges. Low tide occurs in these places because water flowed out of these areas and into the areas of the bulges.

This model describes how the moon's gravitational force causes two bulges of water to form: one pointing toward the moon and one pointing away from the moon. The red dot represents the Bay of Fundy and the blue area around Earth shows how the ocean water forms bulges on two sides of the planet. When the red spot is located between the bulges, the Bay of Fundy experiences low tide. When the red spot is in a bulge, the bay experiences high tide.

2 A.M.
Kayaker is beached

Low tide

8 A.M.
Kayaker is floating

High tide

Rotation, Revolution, and the Tides

When you give the tide chart back to your tour leader, you ask her why the tides follow such a regular, predictable pattern. She tells you that the pattern of the tides is regular because Earth rotates at a constant speed.

As Earth rotates, a different part of Earth moves under the moon, and the part of Earth that is closest to the moon changes. The high tide bulges always point toward the moon and away from the moon, and a given spot on Earth moves in and out of the bulges as Earth rotates.

Remember that Earth rotates once each day and that there are two high tide bulges and two areas of low tide. As shown in the lower panels, during a 24 hour period, a point on Earth goes through a low tide, a high tide, a second low tide, and a second high tide.

Usually 4 tides happen in a day, so it seems as though the tides should be separated by exactly 6 hours. The "extra" 12.5 minutes between tides happen because the moon revolves around Earth. As the moon moves, the bulge moves with it. So a spot on Earth has to move a little bit farther than a quarter turn to get to the next high tide or low tide. The extra 12.5 minutes are why high tide and low tide happen at different times each day. A complete cycle of 2 high tides and 2 low tides takes 24 hours and 50 minutes. If your tour leader plans to go kayaking at high tide every day, she would have to go 50 minutes later each day. She could also consult a tide chart to be sure to avoid kayaking on a dry beach! ◆

A spot on Earth moves in and out of the high tide bulges as Earth rotates. However, the bulges move as the moon revolves around Earth. As the bulge moves, kayakers at the Bay of Fundy experience high tides and low tides. Earth's motion and the moon's motion cause the tides to be separated by a little more than 6 hours.

2 P.M.
Kayaker is beached

Low tide

8 P.M.
Kayaker is floating

High tide

Eclipses

How are lunar and solar eclipses different?

Introduction

You visit a science museum to observe a solar eclipse. You put on your solar eclipse glasses to protect your eyes. As you look up at the sky, the sun slowly darkens. Then the sun brightens again as if nothing ever happened. In ancient times, people used myths to describe this phenomenon. A Hindu myth describes the demon Rahu swallowing the sun or the moon, starting an eclipse. Since Rahu is only a head, after some time, the sun and moon slip out of his throat, and the eclipse ends. Many ancient cultures explain eclipses with myths of creatures eating celestial objects in the sky.

People today enjoy these myths as stories because the scientific explanation for eclipses is well understood. You know that when an eclipse occurs, it is not because a demon is swallowing the sun or the moon. So, what actually causes an eclipse?

Like lunar phases, eclipses are a result of certain repeating patterns in the Earth-sun-moon system. However, eclipses are relatively rare events compared to occurrence of a full moon or a new moon. If you stood in place and looked at the sky for a full year, you would only observe about five eclipses. However, if you counted the number of new moons or full moons you saw over a year, you would see 24 new or full moons. Why are eclipses so rare?

In this lesson, you will learn about the shadows that celestial objects cast and how those shadows cause eclipses of the sun and the moon. You will extend your understanding of the Earth-sun-moon system, using it to explain eclipses of the sun and moon. As you explore this lesson, notice the pattern of changes during an eclipse and how that pattern relates to cause and effect relationships.

Vocabulary

umbra the darker, central part of a shadow

penumbra the lighter part of a shadow that surrounds the umbra

eclipse an event in which the shadow of one celestial object falls on another celestial object

lunar eclipse an eclipse that happens when the moon passes through Earth's shadow

solar eclipse an eclipse that happens when light from the sun is blocked by the moon, and the moon's shadow falls on Earth

Next Generation Science Standards

Performance Expectations
MS-ESS1-1. Develop and use a model of the Earth-sun-moon system to describe the cyclic patterns of lunar phases, eclipses of the sun and moon, and seasons.

Science and Engineering Practices
Developing and Using Models Develop and use a model to describe phenomena.

Crosscutting Concepts
Patterns Patterns can be used to identify cause and effect relationships.
Scientific Knowledge Assumes an Order and Consistency in Natural Systems

Disciplinary Core Ideas
ESS1.B. This model of the solar system can explain eclipses of the sun and the moon. Earth's spin axis is fixed in direction over the short-term but tilted relative to its orbit around the sun. The seasons are a result of that tilt and are caused by the differential intensity of sunlight on different areas of Earth across the year.

1. Celestial Objects Cast Shadows

As you and your friends are walking to school, you notice some younger kids yelling and pointing to the sky. You look up, but the sun is so bright that you have to hold your hand up to block the glare and protect your eyes.

When you put your hand up, you "covered" the sun with your hand. But something else happened, too. Your hand came between the sun and your face, which caused your hand's shadow to fall on your face. However, have you noticed that the shadow is lighter in some parts?

The Umbra and Penumbra Look carefully at the shadow of the toy windmill in Figure 4.1A. Light shining from the right of the picture casts a windmill-shaped shadow on the table. Notice how the shadow looks darker in the middle than it does at the edges. The darker, center part of a shadow is the **umbra**. An umbra cast by any object is dark because the light from a given light source is completely blocked. Suppose a single light was shining on the windmill. When an object, such as a coin, lies in the windmill's umbra, no light will hit the coin. The coin would not be visible as long as it was completely within the windmill's umbra.

Now look carefully at the edges of the shadow cast on the table. The edges of the toy's shadow are not as dark as the center. The part of a shadow that surrounds the umbra and is not as dark as the umbra is the **penumbra**. The penumbra of the shadow is not as dark as its umbra because some light *does* reach that part of the shadow. When an object lies in another object's penumbra, it becomes harder to see, but is still visible. If a coin were in the windmill's penumbra, the coin would appear darker but still visible.

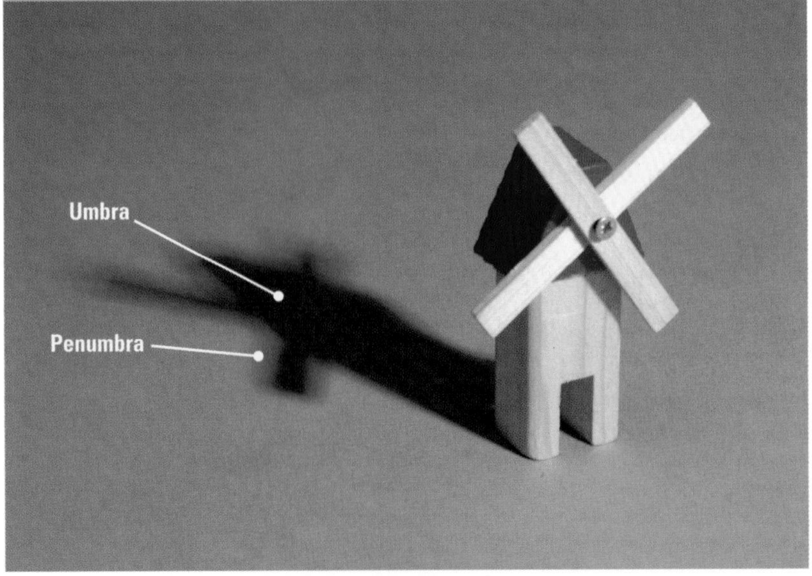

Figure 4.1A

Shadows are not uniformly dark. Here, a windmill casts a shadow on a table. The darker, center part of a shadow is its umbra. The lighter edge of the shadow is its penumbra.

The Two Parts of a Shadow

Umbra

Penumbra

Shadows and Eclipses Similar to how the windmill casts a shadow on a table, celestial bodies also cast shadows. As light from the sun hits Earth, Earth casts a shadow into space. Just like the toy windmill's shadow in Figure 4.1A, the shadow that Earth casts has a dark umbra and a lighter penumbra. An **eclipse** is an event in which the shadow of one celestial object falls on another celestial object. How do celestial objects cast shadows in space?

Figure 4.1B shows the shadow cast by Earth. Earth blocks some light from the sun, and casts a shadow in space on the opposite side of Earth from the sun. Unlike when a windmill casts a shadow onto a flat surface, when Earth casts a shadow into empty space, it does not form the shape of a circle. Instead, it casts a 3-dimensional shadow into space. Earth's umbra has a cone shape because Earth is a sphere. If you were floating in space in Earth's umbra, you would not be able to see the sun. The moon also casts a shadow, and its umbra also has a cone shape because the moon is also a sphere.

Figure 4.1B also shows Earth's penumbra, which is the shadow between the blue lines. Earth's penumbra is shaped like a cone that has its tip cut off. Earth sits in the cut-off tip of the cone. The wide part of the cone points away from Earth and the sun. If you were floating in space in Earth's penumbra, you would see a small sliver of the sun, as if somebody had taken a large bite out of it. The moon has a similarly shaped penumbra.

When celestial objects lie in other celestial objects' umbras and penumbras, eclipses occur. Depending on which celestial object blocks the sun from view, either a lunar or a solar eclipse forms.

Figure 4.1B
Earth blocks some light from the sun and casts a shadow in space on the opposite side of Earth from the sun. The umbra Earth casts in space is in the shape of a 3-dimensional cone, similar to an ice cream cone. The penumbra appears as a cone with its tip cut off.

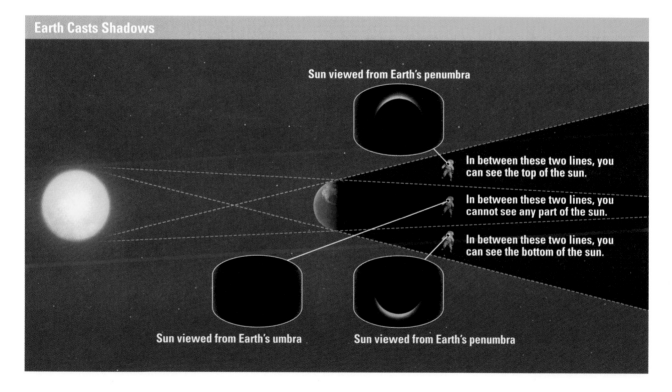

Earth Casts Shadows

Sun viewed from Earth's penumbra

In between these two lines, you can see the top of the sun.

In between these two lines, you cannot see any part of the sun.

In between these two lines, you can see the bottom of the sun.

Sun viewed from Earth's umbra

Sun viewed from Earth's penumbra

2. Lunar Eclipses

As you observe the night sky, you notice something odd. Instead of appearing as a bright white disk in the sky, the moon appears as a blood red disk! What causes such a strange sight?

You have just observed a lunar eclipse! When Earth passes between the sun and the moon, the Earth's shadow can fall on the moon. A **lunar eclipse** is an eclipse that happens when the moon is in Earth's shadow. During a lunar eclipse, the moon slowly grows darker and then appears as a blood red circle. After a while, the moon becomes brighter and returns to normal.

A lunar eclipse starts when the moon begins to enter Earth's penumbra. Because the penumbra is not very dark, the moon dims only slightly. People do not notice any darkening of the moon until most of the moon is in the penumbra.

A lunar eclipse becomes much more noticeable once the moon starts to enter Earth's umbra. At that point, people will see one edge of the moon become dark. More and more of the moon will darken as the moon moves farther into the umbra. A total lunar eclipse, shown in Figure 4.2A, begins once the entire moon is in Earth's umbra. During a total lunar eclipse, people on Earth cannot see the moon because it is entirely in Earth's shadow.

A total lunar eclipse ends when the edge of the moon exits Earth's umbra. Then, the moon passes through Earth's penumbra again. Finally, the moon moves completely out of Earth's shadow, and the lunar eclipse ends. Figure 4.2B shows the stages of a total lunar eclipse as seen from Earth.

Figure 4.2A

A lunar eclipse happens when Earth's shadow falls on the moon. Here, the full moon lies completely in Earth's umbra.

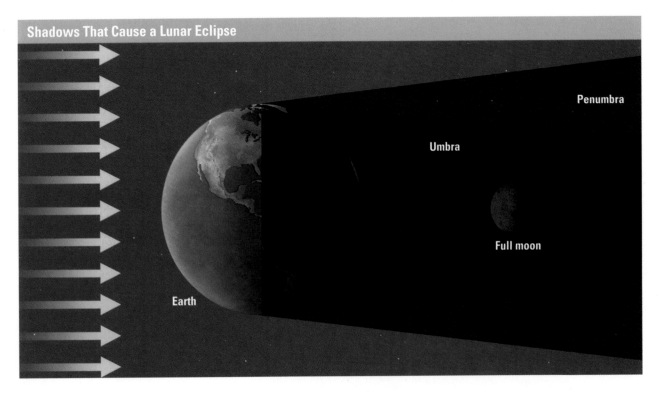

Shadows That Cause a Lunar Eclipse

Penumbra

Umbra

Full moon

Earth

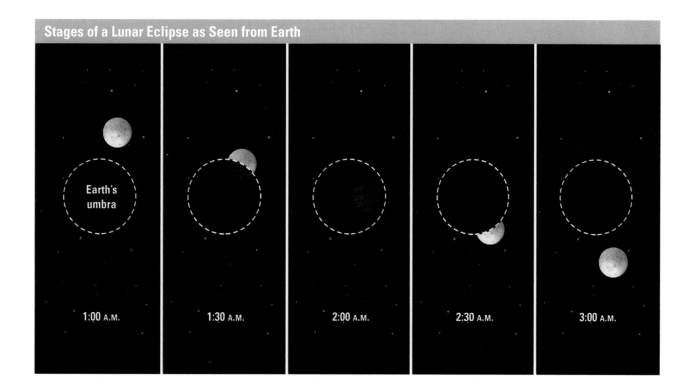

Stages of a Lunar Eclipse as Seen from Earth

Earth's umbra

1:00 A.M. 1:30 A.M. 2:00 A.M. 2:30 A.M. 3:00 A.M.

A *partial lunar eclipse* is similar to a total lunar eclipse. The only difference is that not all of the moon enters Earth's umbra during a partial eclipse. So, the part of the moon that is not in the umbra remains bright. As the moon travels through Earth's umbra, more and more of the moon will darken. However, part of the moon will never enter the umbra. That part of the moon remains bright for the entire eclipse.

Both total lunar eclipses and partial lunar eclipses happen only when Earth is between the sun and the moon. When the sun and the moon are on opposite sides of Earth, the moon is a full moon. As a result, lunar eclipses happen only during full moons.

The hardest part of observing a lunar eclipse is waiting for one to happen. When a lunar eclipse happens, everyone on the night side of Earth can see it. But what time the eclipse happens depends on where you are. Suppose that an eclipse occurs when North America is experiencing night. People in California may see the total eclipse start around midnight, but people in New York would see the same total eclipse starting around 3 A.M.

You might expect the moon to appear black or dark gray during a total lunar eclipse, but sometimes, the moon looks red. Why does it appear red? The moon appears red because of Earth's atmosphere. Earth blocks most of the sunlight, but some sunlight passes through Earth's atmosphere. Sunlight is made of different colors. As red light passes through the atmosphere, it is bent so that a little bit ends up shining on the moon, which makes the moon look red. When the moon is red during an eclipse, some people call it a "blood moon."

Figure 4.2B

During a lunar eclipse, the moon passes through Earth's umbra. As the moon passes through, it becomes less visible until it is completely in Earth's umbra. The moon may appear red at this time. As it exits Earth's umbra, parts of the moon can be seen, until the whole moon is visible again.

3. Solar Eclipses

Centuries ago, children were hurried indoors in the middle of the day and the windows were covered. What was going on outside that they were not allowed to see?

Like Earth, the moon casts a shadow because the moon blocks light from the sun. When the moon is between Earth and the sun, the moon's shadow can fall on Earth. A **solar eclipse** is an eclipse that happens when light from the sun is blocked by the moon, and the moon's shadow falls on Earth.

During a solar eclipse, the sun grows darker and seems to change shape. The sun may disappear from view before returning to normal. What a person sees during a solar eclipse depends on what part of the moon's shadow the person is standing in.

As long as a location on Earth remains in the moon's penumbra, observers at that location will see a *partial* solar eclipse. A solar eclipse starts when the sun appears to have a small "bite" taken out of its side. The observer is standing in the edge of the moon's penumbra. The moon's shadow keeps moving, and the location on Earth goes farther in to the penumbra. More and more of the sun is blocked. This means that only part of the sun will appear to be covered by the moon.

When the moon's umbra reaches a location on Earth, people there will see a *total* solar eclipse. Figure 4.3A shows how shadows cause a solar eclipse. The moon completely blocks the view of the sun. People will see a dark disk (the moon) surrounded by a glowing ring. The glowing ring is the sun's corona, as you saw in the beginning of the lesson, which is the upper part of the sun's atmosphere.

Figure 4.3A

A solar eclipse happens when the moon's shadow falls on Earth. The moon's penumbra forms a large circle on Earth's surface, and the moon's umbra forms a smaller circle inside the penumbra. People and animals located within the moon's penumbra observe a particle solar eclipse, while a location in the moon's umbra observes a total solar eclipse.

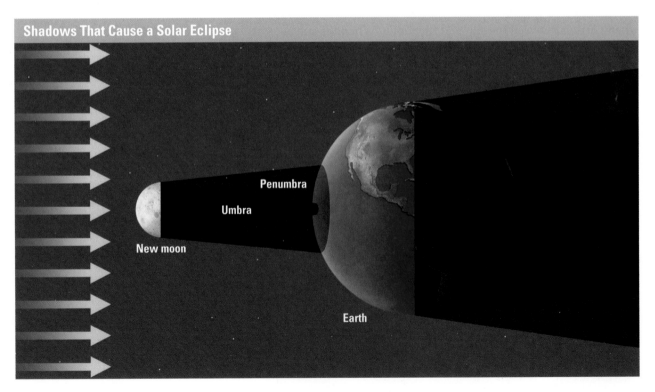

Shadows That Cause a Solar Eclipse

New moon

Umbra

Penumbra

Earth

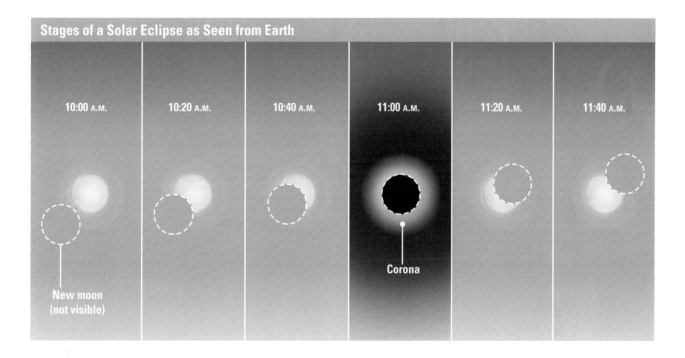

Stages of a Solar Eclipse as Seen from Earth

10:00 A.M.   10:20 A.M.   10:40 A.M.   11:00 A.M.   11:20 A.M.   11:40 A.M.

Corona

New moon
(not visible)

The moon's umbra only covers a small portion of Earth's surface, and it moves quickly. So, total solar eclipses do not last for long for a given location on Earth. They normally last for only 5 minutes. Once the umbra moves past a location on Earth, the location enters the penumbra again. The edge of the sun appears, and people see a partial solar eclipse again. As the penumbra moves away, more and more of the sun is uncovered. Once the location on Earth is no longer in any part of the moon's shadow, the eclipse ends and the sun returns to its normal appearance and brightness. Figure 4.3B shows the stages of a solar eclipse as seen from Earth.

Solar eclipses happen when the moon is between Earth and the sun. This means they only happen during the new moon phase. This is because the sun, Earth, and moon need to align, and the sun and moon are only on the same side of Earth during the new moon phase.

You are less likely to see a solar eclipse than a lunar eclipse because the path of the moon's shadow is narrow compared to the size of Earth. The moon is much smaller than Earth, so the moon's shadow covers just a small part of Earth's surface. Since only people inside the moon's shadow can see a solar eclipse, only a small part of the world can see a particular solar eclipse. Also, solar eclipses do not last for very long. A partial solar eclipse may last for a few hours, but total solar eclipses only last for a few minutes, if they even appear.

You must have special tools to see a partial solar eclipse safely. Looking directly at the sun can damage your eyes, even during an eclipse. Though centuries ago, children were sometimes kept indoors during a solar eclipse, now it is safe to stay outdoors and observe an eclipse as long as you are using proper equipment, such as glasses with special lenses or a pinhole viewer!

Figure 4.3B

The appearance of the sun changes during a solar eclipse. The edge of the sun begins to "disappear" as the moon comes between Earth and the sun. Less and less of the sun is visible until the moon completely obscures the sun. At that time, the sun's corona is noticeable. Then more of the sun becomes visible as the moon moves and obscures less of the sun.

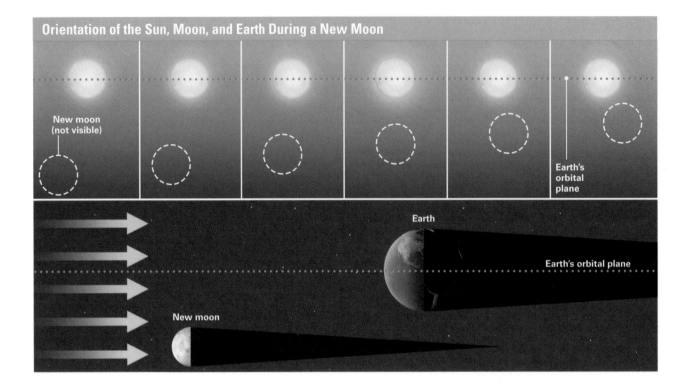

Orientation of the Sun, Moon, and Earth During a New Moon

New moon
(not visible)

Earth's
orbital
plane

Earth

Earth's orbital plane

New moon

Figure 4.4A

Eclipses can only occur when the moon's orbit intersects with Earth's orbital plane. When the new moon is not in line with Earth's orbital plane, a solar eclipse does not occur. Here, the new moon lies below Earth's orbital plane and no eclipse occurs.

4. The Moon's Orbit and Earth's Orbital Plane

The sun, the moon, and Earth must line up on the same plane for Earth's shadow to fall on the moon. The same must happen for the moon's shadow to fall on Earth. So when do they line up?

The moon revolves around Earth about once a month. So, it seems as though Earth, the sun, and the moon should line up twice each month. You would expect to see a solar eclipse during every new moon, and a lunar eclipse during every full moon. But that is not what happens.

The moon's orbit is tilted compared to Earth's orbital plane. Recall that an orbit is the path an object follows as it revolves around another object and that an orbital plane is the imaginary flat surface in which an orbit lies. Because the moon's orbit is tilted, the moon only intersects with Earth's orbital plane twice a month, when the moon crosses the orbital plane from above to below, and from below to above. The moon may or may not intersect with Earth's orbital plane during a new moon or a full moon. If the moon crosses the orbital plane during either the full moon or the new moon, an eclipse occurs. Otherwise, there will be no eclipse that month.

Most months, the new moon or full moon does not intersect with Earth's orbital plane. Instead, the moon is above or below Earth's orbital plane during these two phases. The bottom panel of figure 4.4A shows the new moon's shadow missing Earth because it is below the orbital plane. The top panel shows how the new moon passes through the sky without blocking the sun, which sits on Earth's orbital plane. The shadows cast by the new moon do not land on Earth.

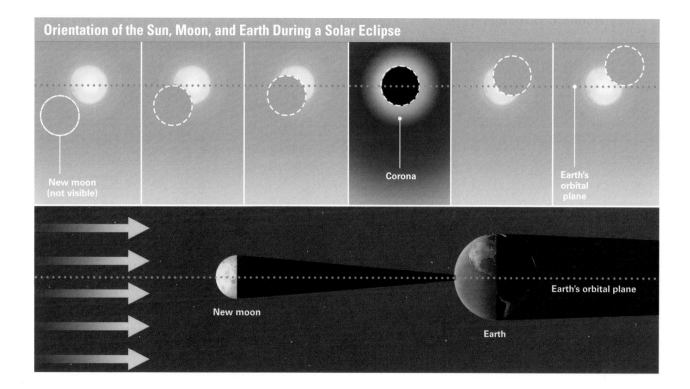

Orientation of the Sun, Moon, and Earth During a Solar Eclipse

New moon (not visible)

Corona

Earth's orbital plane

New moon

Earth

Earth's orbital plane

However, a few times a year, the new moon or full moon will pass through Earth's orbital plane. Figure 4.4B shows the new moon as it passes through Earth's orbital plane. As it travels along its tilted orbit, it goes from lying below Earth's orbital plane to lying on Earth's orbital plane. When this happens, it "covers" the sun, causing an eclipse. As the moon continues its orbit, it travels above Earth's orbital plane, and the sun becomes visible again. The bottom panel of Figure 4.4B shows that when the new moon lies on Earth's orbital plane, it casts a shadow directly on Earth that "covers" the sun.

Likewise, a lunar eclipse occurs when a full moon passes through Earth's orbital plane. As the full moon travels through its orbit, Earth's shadow covers it when the full moon crosses Earth's orbital plane. As the moon continues through its orbit, Earth's shadow shines in space above or below the full moon, and the full moon appears again.

An eclipse only occurs when the sun, the moon, and Earth line up perfectly. These perfect arrangements do not happen very often. Usually, only two partial solar eclipses and two partial lunar eclipses happen each year, though some years may have more. Even if an eclipse occurs, it does not mean that you will be able to see it from your location. Seeing an eclipse is made harder by the fact that you have to be on the right part of Earth to see it. If an eclipse is occurring in China, you will not be able to see it from the United States.

So, if you have a chance to view an eclipse, you should! You can find out when the next eclipse will happen by looking it up on the Internet. Some websites give the dates and locations of both solar eclipses and lunar eclipses.

Figure 4.4B

For an eclipse to occur, the moon must be in the new moon or full moon position, and the moon's orbit must line up on the Earth's orbital plane. Here, the new moon sits on Earth's orbital plane, causing a solar eclipse.

Eclipses and the Orbital Plane

An eclipse happens when Earth's shadow falls on the moon or when the moon's shadow falls on Earth. A solar eclipse only occurs during a new moon, and a lunar eclipse only occurs during a full moon. Eclipses can only happen when Earth, the sun, and the full or new moon lie in the same plane, or flat surface. Look closely for where the moon's orbit overlaps with the orbital plane to observe the cause of an eclipse.

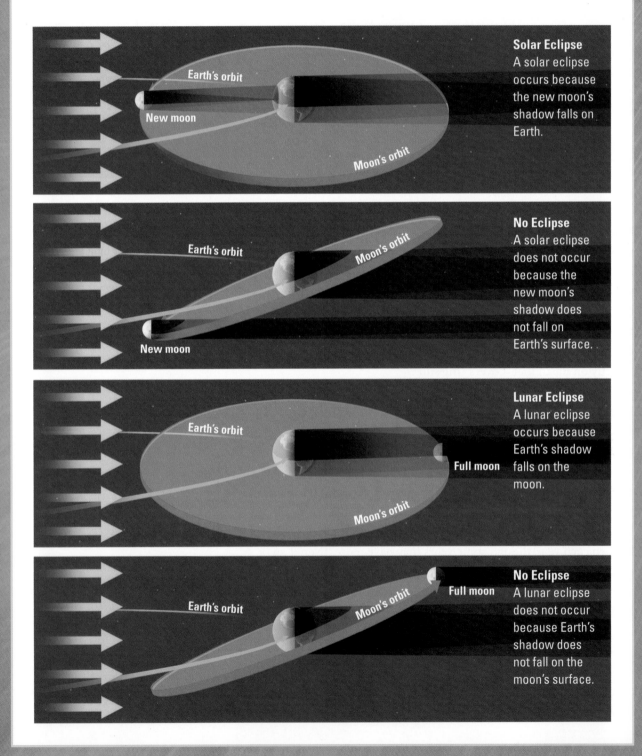

Solar Eclipse
A solar eclipse occurs because the new moon's shadow falls on Earth.

Earth's orbit

New moon

Moon's orbit

No Eclipse
A solar eclipse does not occur because the new moon's shadow does not fall on Earth's surface.

Earth's orbit

Moon's orbit

New moon

Lunar Eclipse
A lunar eclipse occurs because Earth's shadow falls on the moon.

Earth's orbit

Full moon

Moon's orbit

No Eclipse
A lunar eclipse does not occur because Earth's shadow does not fall on the moon's surface.

Earth's orbit

Moon's orbit

Full moon

5. The Apparent Sizes of the Sun and the Moon

Suppose you had a quarter and held it up toward a lamp. When you do so, the quarter appears to cover up the lamp. The quarter is much smaller than the lamp, yet it blocks the lamp from view. Why?

In general, objects that are farther away from you look smaller than objects that are closer to you. Look at the photo of the man and the woman with the umbrella. It appears as though the woman is very small and that the man is holding the woman up by her legs. However, the man and the woman are actually about the same size. The woman is merely standing very far away, which causes her to appear much smaller than the man.

The same optical illusion happens with the sun and moon during solar eclipses. Though the sun's diameter is about 400 times larger than the moon's diameter, the sun is also about 400 times farther away than the moon. If the sun were the size of a basketball, the moon would be about the size of a speck of dust. However, if the basketball were hundreds of meters away, it would appear about as small as a pinhead held up to your face. So, when seen from Earth, the sun and the moon seem to be the same size!

Because the sun and the moon appear to be the same size, solar eclipses look spectacular. The moon covers up the main part of the sun, leaving only the glowing corona visible. But the perfect size match also means that total solar eclipses do not last for very long.

Though the man and the woman are about the same size, the woman appears much smaller because she is further away. Similarly, though the sun is much larger than the moon, the sun appears to be the same size as the moon from Earth because it is also much further away.

LESSON SUMMARY

Eclipses

Celestial Objects Cast Shadows An eclipse happens when the shadow of one celestial object falls on a second celestial object. Every shadow is made of a dark umbra and a lighter penumbra.

Lunar Eclipses A lunar eclipse happens when Earth's shadow falls on a full moon.

Solar Eclipses A solar eclipse happens when a new moon blocks the sun and casts a shadow on Earth. Only people inside the moon's shadow can see the eclipse.

The Moon's Orbit and Earth's Orbital Plane Eclipses do not happen very often because the moon's orbit is tilted compared to Earth's orbital plane. An eclipse only occurs when a full moon or a new moon crosses Earth's orbital plane.

The Apparent Sizes of the Sun and the Moon The sun and the moon appear to be the same size because the sun is 400 times larger than the moon and is 400 times farther away. This allows the moon to cover the sun when seen from Earth.

A Soaring Science Lab

High up in space, the huge International Space Station revolves around Earth every 90 minutes. Lit up with 4,000 square meters of solar panels, it can be the second brightest spot in the night sky next to the moon. It is both a home and a workplace to its crew of astronauts. What is the International Space Station, and what kinds of work and research go on there?

Launched in 1998, the International Space Station (ISS) is a habitable artificial satellite and huge international project. People from more than a dozen countries around the world have lived and worked together on the ISS since 2000. The ISS is enormous—on Earth, it weighs more than 400,000 kg and is almost as long as a football field. The ISS is the largest human-made object in orbit around Earth and is so large that you can see it from Earth with the unaided eye.

Though the ISS is almost as long as a football field, it is much smaller than the moon. However, it is much closer, located right outside Earth's atmosphere. Like the moon, the ISS can cast shadows on Earth to form eclipses. Can you find the umbra and penumbra of the shadow cast by the ISS?

Astronauts live and work on the International Space Station. An astronaut took this photo of Earth in 2006. From the ISS, astronauts can see Earth quite clearly, just as people on Earth can see the ISS.

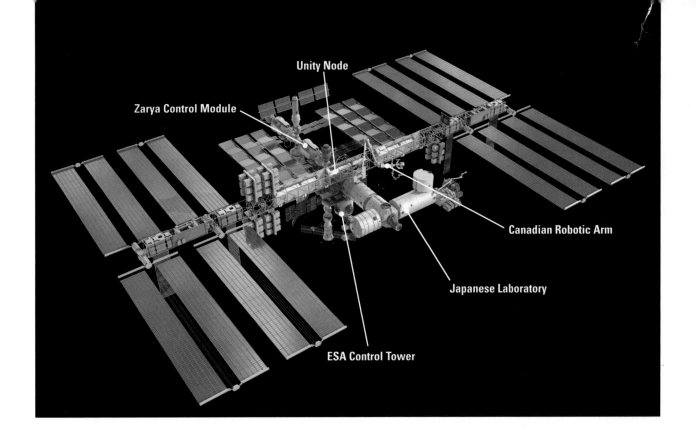

Unity Node

Zarya Control Module

Canadian Robotic Arm

Japanese Laboratory

ESA Control Tower

An International Effort

The idea of having several countries work together to build a space station was first proposed in 1982. The United States asked Japan, Canada, and several European countries to participate in the project. They envisioned the space station to be an orbiting science laboratory and a place to learn about space travel in general. Years of planning and design followed, and more countries, including Russia, joined the project.

The ISS was too big to be launched into space in one piece, so the various countries designed, built, and sent up parts of the station separately. In 1998, the Russians launched the first component of the ISS into orbit. That piece was the Zarya Control Module, which stores battery power and fuel and has places for spacecraft to dock. The United States attached the second piece of the ISS, the Unity Node, later that same year. That piece was a utility node, a space module with several docking ports, that is used to join other pieces to the station.

The ISS continued to be constructed over the next several years. In that time, more than 40 missions took pieces up to space and attached them to the station. The pieces included a giant robotic arm from Canada, a laboratory module from Japan, and a control tower with seven windows from the European Space Agency. The ISS was considered fully assembled by 2011, but the station is still able to grow if needed. New modules can be attached, and old modules can be moved around or replaced.

Many countries built parts of the ISS. Engineers from the various countries worked together to design modules that could be attached together and perform different functions. For example, the Japanese experiment module is designed for performing science research in various fields including space medicine, Earth observations, and communications.

Science and Technology in Space

Although the International Space Station wasn't fully assembled until 2011, people have been living on it since 2000. What do the astronauts do during their time in space? Many of them carry out science experiments.

Astronauts on the ISS conduct experiments in many fields of science, including biology, chemistry, Earth science, and physics. Some experiments they have conducted have included studying how microgravity affects plants, determining the best methods for putting out fires in space, and tracking air pollution from orbit. The astronauts also do technology research to help engineers on Earth.

One of the long-term technology research projects on the ISS is Robonaut 2—a robotic astronaut. Robonaut 2, or R2, joined the crew on the station in 2011. Since then, the astronauts have been testing R2's systems and controls and have been putting the robot to work.

R2 was designed to have a similar shape to a human so that it could perform tasks as a human would. For example, R2's hands look and move like human hands so that the robot can use the same tools that a person uses. Engineers hope that R2 will eventually take over repetitive maintenance jobs on the ISS to free up the astronauts' time to do their science research.

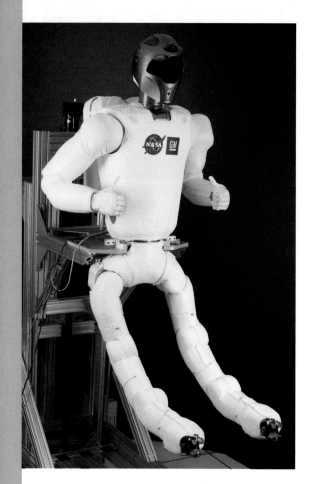

Robonaut 2 is a robotic astronaut that is currently being tested on the ISS. Astronauts and engineers hope that the robot will eventually take over some of the maintenance tasks on the station so that astronauts are free for collecting scientific data.

R2's first job was to measure the airflow from vents on the ISS. The robot does this job very well because the job involves holding a tool very still and not breathing on it. Holding still and not breathing are two things that R2 does much better than a human.

During R2's first few years on the ISS, it stood on a pole and was moved around as needed. However, in 2014, the robot got legs. Unlike R2's hands and arms, its legs and feet are very different from their human counterparts. Each leg has seven joints (a human leg has three main joints), and the joints can bend and twist in ways that human joints cannot. R2's "feet" are actually clamps. People on the station don't walk on the floor—they float around. R2's clamp-feet allow the robot to grab handrails and pull itself around the International Space Station.

Astronauts collect data about R2's performance and send it to engineers on Earth who use the data to improve the design of R2 and of robots on Earth. They hope that R2 will be able to perform more jobs on the ISS and that robots will be able to help people with physical disabilities.

Use the Force, ISS

Another engineering research project on the ISS was inspired by the movie *Star Wars: A New Hope.* A college professor challenged his students to design an object similar to the moving, floating sphere used for lightsaber training in that movie. The students' design eventually became the SPHERES project, which stands for Synchronized Position Hold, Engage, Reorient, Experimental Satellites. Three SPHERES were sent to the ISS for testing.

Each sphere is about the size of a volleyball and contains a computer, a battery, a radio for receiving and sending signals, and tiny thrusters to make it move around. Initially, the SPHERES were used to test how well computer programs could control their motion. They have also been used to test flying in unison and docking procedures.

The SPHERES have ports, which can be used to attach tools or other parts for future experiments. Scientists from around the world were invited to design experiments for the SPHERES. Scientists interested in using the SPHERES work with the project engineers and the ISS astronauts to design and carry out their experiments.

The SPHERES project is a great example of the mission of the International Space Station. The project is collaborative and international, and its purpose is to conduct science and technology research. However, no one has yet designed a *Star Wars*-inspired lightsaber to test how well the SPHERES can avoid being hit! ◆

The three SPHERES are part of a research project on the ISS. Each sphere is a different color. The astronauts can control the movement of the SPHERES by using a computer.

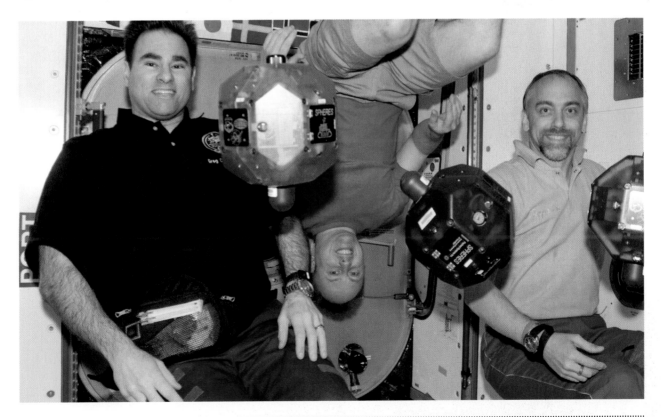

The Solar System

OVERVIEW

What celestial bodies are in our solar system, and how can you compare them? In this unit, you will describe the role of gravity in the solar system. You will also compare the characteristics of different solar system objects using data collected from telescopes on Earth and in space and spacecraft that fly into the far reaches of space to send back information. You will work to organize, analyze, and present the data in the form of a strong argument on how to classify the planets of the solar system.

UNIT CONTENTS

Performance Assessment
Organize and analyze the data you collected to create a convincing argument on how to classify the celestial bodies of the solar system.

UNIT 2

Performance Expectations

MS-ESS1-2. Develop and use a model to describe the role of gravity in the motions within galaxies and the solar system.

MS-ESS1-3. Analyze and interpret data to determine scale properties of objects in the solar system.

MS-ETS1-2. Evaluate competing design solutions using a systematic process to determine how well they meet the criteria and constraints of the problem.

MS-ETS1- 3. Analyze data from tests to determine similarities and differences among several design solutions to identify the best characteristics of each that can be combined into a new solution to better meet the criteria for success.

Science and Engineering Practices

Developing and Using Models
Develop and use a model to describe phenomena.

Analyzing and Interpreting Data
Analyze and interpret data to determine similarities and differences in findings.

Engaging in Argument from Evidence
Evaluate competing design solutions based on jointly developed and agreed-upon design criteria.

Crosscutting Concepts

Scale, Proportion, and Quantity
Time, space, and energy phenomena can be observed at various scales using models to study systems that are too large or too small.

Systems and System Models
Models can be used to represent systems and their interactions.

Connections to Engineering, Technology, and Applications of Science: Interdependence of Science, Engineering, and Technology
Engineering advances have led to important discoveries in virtually every field of science and scientific discoveries have led to the development of entire industries and engineered systems.

Disciplinary Core Ideas

ESS1.B. Earth and the Solar System
The solar system consists of the sun and a collection of objects, including planets, their moons, and asteroids that are held in orbit around the sun by its gravitational pull on them.

ETS1.B. Developing Possible Solutions
• There are systematic processes for evaluating solutions with respect to how well they meet the criteria and constraints of a problem.
• Sometimes parts of different solutions can be combined to create a solution that is better than any of its predecessors.

ETS1.C. Optimizing the Design Solution
Although one design may not perform the best across all tests, identifying the characteristics of the design that performed the best in each test can provide useful information for the redesign process—that is, some of those characteristics may be incorporated into the new design.

Connect Your Learning

Have you ever thought about living on Venus? The idea of living on another planet might excite you, but the acidic atmosphere that surrounds Venus wouldn't! Though the planets and other celestial bodies of the solar system appear as tiny pinpricks in the sky, using different tools, scientists can study far-away celestial bodies. Collecting, analyzing, and interpreting data allows them to better understand the phenomena of how objects in the solar system are similar and different for future exploration.

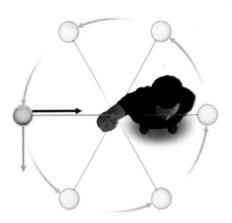

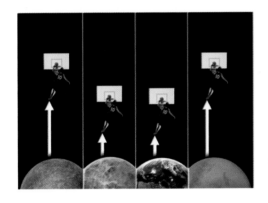

The Solar System

Forces keep the planets in motion around the sun. How does twirling a ball on the end of a string around your head model the motion of planets in the solar system?

Have you always wished you could jump higher on the basketball court? You could if there were an inner solar system league. How much higher could you jump on Mars than on Earth?

When planning a family vacation, you know that if you forget something, you can always buy it along the way. Not so for space travel. NASA engineers had to plan everything in advance before sending Pioneer 10 to the outer solar system. What other worries did they have that you don't usually think about while traveling on Earth?

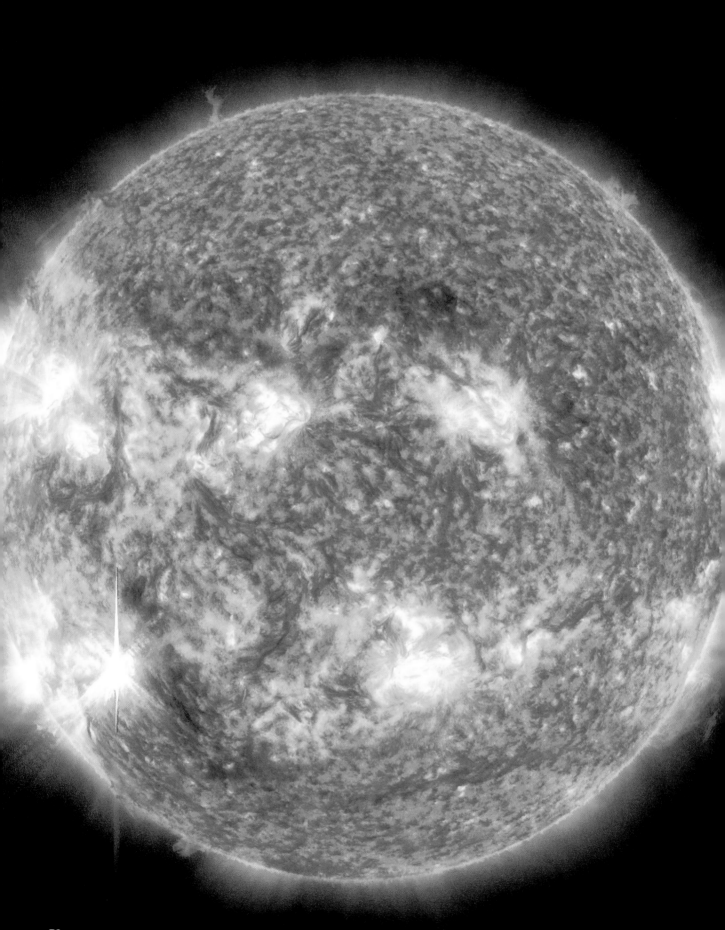

Gravity and the Solar System

How is the solar system held together?

Introduction

This close-up photo of the sun doesn't even begin to help you understand how huge it is! How massive is the sun? The sun is a star and is the largest object in our solar system. If all other objects in the solar system were added together, they would still be 500 times smaller than the sun! But despite the sun's huge mass, the sun does not take up much space in the solar system. How does this massive sun hold together the planets and other objects in the solar system?

The planets and other objects in the solar system are spread out over vast distances. What do these celestial objects look like from Earth? Planets much larger than Earth look like dots in the sky because they are so far away. The ancient Greeks and Romans observed these tiny pinpricks of light as they moved in the night sky and named them after their gods and goddesses. One of our nearby planets is named Mars, after the Roman god of war. Another planet is named Venus, after the Roman goddess of beauty. How does the size of these planets affect their location and appearance in our solar system?

Previously, you learned about the Earth-sun-moon system. Now, you will explore the solar system, which includes not only Earth, the sun, and the moon, but also the nearby planets, dwarf planets, and comets. You will learn how gravitational forces hold the different components of the solar system together and how to use a scale model to understand the size of the solar system.

Vocabulary

gravitational force an attractive force between all objects that have mass

solar system a star and all the objects that travel around it

planet an object that directly revolves around a star, has a nearly spherical shape, and has cleared the neighborhood around its orbit

moon a celestial object that indirectly revolves around a star

comet a small object made of rock, ice, and dust that has a highly elliptical orbit around the sun and gives off gas and dust in a tail as it travels close to the sun

asteroid a small rocky or metallic object that revolves around the sun

dwarf planet a celestial object that directly revolves around the sun, has a nearly spherical shape, but has not cleared the neighborhood around its orbit

astronomical unit a unit of measurement equal to the average distance between Earth and the sun; about 150 million km

scale model a representation of a system that has the same relative sizes or distances as the actual system

Next Generation Science Standards

Performance Expectations

MS-ESS1-2. Develop and use a model to describe the role of gravity in the motions within galaxies and the solar system.

MS-ESS1-3. Analyze and interpret data to determine scale properties of objects in the solar system.

Science and Engineering Practices

Developing and Using Models Develop and use a model to describe phenomena.

Analyzing and Interpreting Data Analyze and interpret data to determine similarities and differences in findings.

Crosscutting Concepts

Scale, Proportion, and Quantity Time, space, and energy phenomena can be observed at various scales using models to study systems that are too large or too small.

Systems and System Models Models can be used to represent systems and their interactions.

Disciplinary Core Ideas

ESS1.B. The solar system consists of the sun and a collection of objects, including planets, their moons, and asteroids that are held in orbit around the sun by its gravitational pull on them.

Relative Sizes of the Sun and Earth

Earth

Sun

Figure 5.1

The more massive an object is, the more gravitational force it applies on other objects. The sun is a massive star in the center of the solar system. Earth may seem very large to you, but it is tiny compared to the sun.

1. The Solar System and Gravitational Forces

Suppose you tried to play basketball on the moon. When you jump, you realize you can leap far higher than you can on Earth. You may have heard people say that this is because gravity is weaker on the moon, but how does one object have less gravity than another?

A **gravitational force** is an attractive force between all objects that have mass. For example, you and Earth have mass, and the gravitational force between you and Earth pulls you and Earth together. If you jump up, you come back down because the gravitational force pulls you toward Earth.

The strength of a gravitational force depends on two things: mass and distance. The gravitational force between the objects increases as the masses of the objects increase. If you were standing on the moon, you would experience less gravitational force than if you were standing on Earth. This is because the moon is less massive than Earth.

The strength of gravitational force also depends on the distance between masses. Gravitational force decreases quickly as the distance between the objects increases. The planet Venus has less mass than Earth, so you might expect the gravitational force between Venus and the sun to be less than the force between Earth and the sun. But Venus is closer to the sun than Earth, so the gravitational force between it and the sun is greater than the gravitational force between Earth and the sun.

Gravitational forces between celestial objects hold together our entire solar system. A **solar system** is made up of a star and all the objects that travel around it. The star in our solar system is the sun. Objects that travel around the sun include Earth, other planets, dwarf planets, moons, and many smaller objects.

Gravitational forces may seem to be strong because they hold huge planets together in the solar system. However, most gravitational forces are actually very weak. Only very massive objects exert gravitational forces strong enough to notice. Earth is massive, so you feel and see the effects of its gravitational force. On the other hand, people do not have large masses. So, you do not notice gravity pulling you toward your classmates when you pass them in the hall. The sun contains 99.8% of the mass of the solar system. The sun's large mass means that large gravitational forces exist between the sun and other objects in the solar system. These large gravitational forces are what hold all other objects in the solar system in orbit around the sun.

2. Earth Revolves Because of the Gravitational Force

"Catch!" your friend says as he tosses a ball so it falls in front of you at your feet. By throwing a ball, your friend exerted a force on the ball; this force caused it to change its motion from still to moving. Gravitational forces can also change objects' motion. In fact, the gravitational force between the ball and Earth made the ball fall to the ground.

Forces can change an object's motion in other ways. Suppose that you tie a string around a ball and twirl the ball over your head. The ball moves in a circle because the string exerts a force on the ball, which pulls the ball toward your hand. However, the ball is moving fast enough that it is not pulled into your hand; it just keeps moving around your hand.

Something similar happens in the solar system. The gravitational force between the sun and Earth pulls on Earth, but Earth is not pulled into the sun. Instead, Earth moves perpendicularly at a very high speed, about 30 km/s, while being pulled by the force. As a result, Earth constantly moves so that it revolves around the sun. If Earth was not moving as quickly, it would fall toward the sun until they collided.

Figure 5.2 models how gravity causes Earth to revolve around the sun. The right side of the figure shows the direction that Earth is moving and the direction that the gravitational force pulls on Earth. If the gravitational force were not there, Earth would move off in a straight line in the direction of the red arrow. The gravitational force, shown by the black arrow, is nearly perpendicular to the direction that Earth moves. The force makes Earth change directions. But even as Earth changes directions, the force keeps pulling perpendicularly to the direction it is moving. Thus, Earth constantly changes directions and moves in a nearly circular orbit, as shown on the figure's right side.

Figure 5.2

The sun's gravitational force pulls on Earth as Earth travels quickly through space. The force causes Earth to "fall around" the sun in a slightly elliptical orbit.

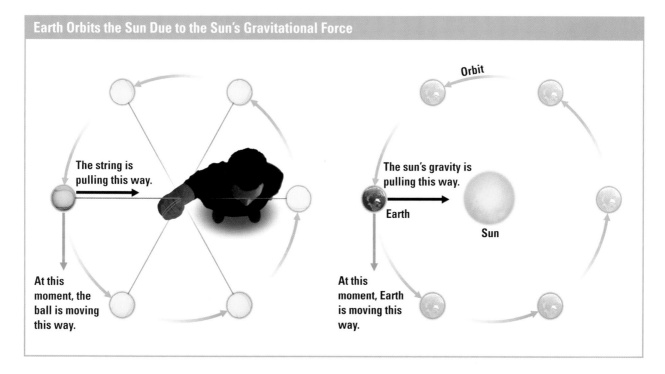

Earth Orbits the Sun Due to the Sun's Gravitational Force

The string is pulling this way.

At this moment, the ball is moving this way.

Orbit

The sun's gravity is pulling this way.

Earth

Sun

At this moment, Earth is moving this way.

3. The Planets

Earth revolves around the sun because of the gravitational force between them. However, Earth is not the only object in orbit around the sun. Trillions of objects revolve around the sun. Which of those trillions of objects are the solar system's planets?

My Very Eager Mother Just Served Us Nachos. That odd sentence can help you remember the names and order of the eight planets as shown in Figure 5.3. The planets are, in order by their distances from the sun: Mercury, Venus, Earth, Mars, Jupiter, Saturn, Uranus, and Neptune. A **planet** is an object that directly revolves around a star, has a nearly spherical shape, and has cleared the neighborhood around its orbit.

A celestial object clears its neighborhood if it is massive enough to attract matter to the object as it moves. The object sweeps up pieces of matter around it. The matter becomes part of the object, begins to revolve around the object, or is pulled into a different orbit.

Gravity also makes planets nearly spherical. Gravitational forces in a very large object pull all the matter in the object toward its center. As a result, the object becomes a sphere.

An object directly revolves around a star if it revolves only around the star. Many objects that are not planets directly revolve around the sun. They are not planets because they are not spherical or they have not cleared their neighborhoods, or both.

Thus, gravity plays a big role in determining what objects are planets. Gravitational forces pull a planet into orbit around a star, give a planet its spherical shape, and clear the neighborhood of a planet's orbit.

Figure 5.3

The planets of the solar system are the eight large objects that directly revolve around the sun. All planets are nearly round and have cleared the neighborhood around their orbits.

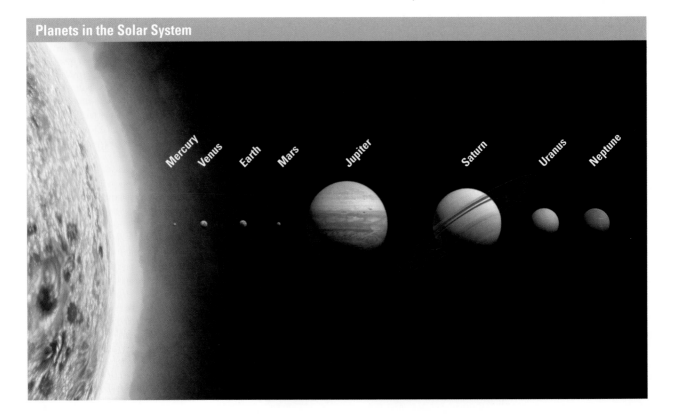

Planets in the Solar System

Mercury · Venus · Earth · Mars · Jupiter · Saturn · Uranus · Neptune

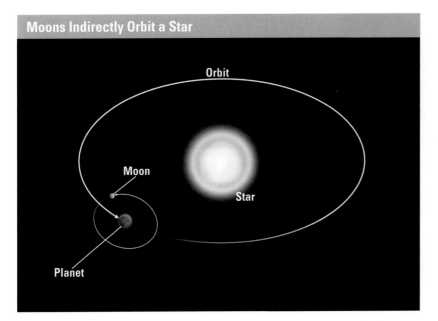

Moons Indirectly Orbit a Star

Orbit

Moon

Star

Planet

Figure 5.4A

Earth's moon is one of many moons in the solar system. The moons in the solar system travel around the sun indirectly. They revolve around celestial objects that are not the sun. These celestial objects, in turn, revolve around the sun.

4. Moons Revolve Around Planets

If the planets directly revolve around the sun, what is something that *indirectly* revolves around the sun? The moon! Earth's moon is just one of about 150 moons in indirect orbit around the sun.

Look at Figure 5.4A. A **moon** is a celestial object that indirectly revolves around a star. A moon is sometimes called a *natural satellite*. A satellite is an object that revolves around a celestial body. All moons are natural satellites, which means that humans did not make them. Artificial satellites are objects made by humans that revolve around a planet. Examples of artificial satellites are GPS satellites, the Hubble Space Telescope, and the International Space Station.

The planets in the solar system have different numbers of moons. Mercury and Venus do not have any moons. Earth has one moon, and Mars has two moons. Jupiter, Saturn, Uranus, and Neptune have many more moons. They may even have moons that have yet to be discovered.

Figure 5.4B shows that Jupiter, Saturn, Uranus, and Neptune have so many moons that each planet and its moons form a system that resembles a mini solar system. Like a star in a solar system, the planet in a group of moons is the largest object. In a solar system, the planets revolve around a star because of the strong gravitational forces between the star and the planets. In a system of moons, the moons revolve around a celestial body because of the strong gravitational forces between the celestial body and the moons.

Systems of moons form only around planets that are very massive. This is because more massive planets exert much stronger gravitational forces on nearby celestial objects than small planets do. These stronger forces allow the large planets to hold more celestial objects in stable orbits. Jupiter is the most massive planet and exerts the strongest gravitational forces among the planets. It also has the most moons.

Figure 5.4B

Planets in the solar system have different number of moons around them, as shown in this table.

Planet	Confirmed Moons
Mercury	0
Venus	0
Earth	1
Mars	2
Jupiter	67
Saturn	62
Uranus	27
Neptune	14

Saturn's moon, Mimas

Dwarf Planet Pluto

Asteroid 433 Eros

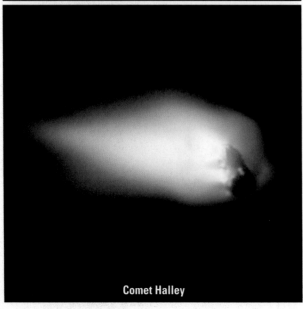

Comet Halley

5. Dwarf Planets, Asteroids, and Comets

In 1801, Italian astronomer Giuseppe Piazza discovered a celestial object that he named Ceres. At first, he thought Ceres was a comet. Then, he thought it might be a planet. Later, British astronomer William Herschel called Ceres and similar objects asteroids. But Ceres's story did not end there. In 2006, astronomers named Ceres as one of the solar system's dwarf planets. Dwarf planets, asteroids, and comets are objects smaller than planets that revolve around the sun.

Dwarf Planets Dwarf planets are similar to planets but with one difference. A **dwarf planet** is a celestial object that directly revolves around the sun, has a nearly round shape, but has not cleared the neighborhood around its orbit. For example, Pluto revolves around the sun and has a nearly round shape. Pluto shares its orbit with many large objects such as asteroids, so it has not cleared its neighborhood.

Asteroids An **asteroid** is a small rocky or metallic object that revolves around the sun. Most of the asteroids in our solar system are found between the orbits of Mars and Jupiter in the main asteroid belt. Asteroids do not have to be spherical. The asteroid belt contains tens of thousands of known asteroids, and probably many more undiscovered asteroids, which are very small and have tiny masses compared to the planets. Some are bigger than mountains, but some are as small as a classroom.

Comets A **comet** is a small object made of rock, ice, and dust that revolves around the sun. Like asteroids, comets do not have to be spherical. Comets give off gas and dust in a tail as they travel close to the sun. Comets usually follow elliptical orbits that are not very circular. Instead, their orbits are long and skinny with the sun near one end.

Dwarf planets, asteroids, and comets are other celestial bodies in our solar system that revolve around the sun.

6. Modeling Distances in the Solar System

Why haven't humans visited different planets? One reason is because the other planets in the solar system are very far away from Earth. The closest one is tens of millions of kilometers away. That would take you several months to a year to reach it using the spacecraft technology available today!

The distances in the solar system are so large that a unit of measurement was developed to describe the solar system. An **astronomical unit** (AU) is equal to the average distance between Earth and the sun. One AU is about 150 million km. The distances between the sun and the other planets range from about 0.4 AU to 30 AU.

You can use a scale model to help understand the distance from the sun to the planets' orbits. A **scale model** is a model of a system that has the same relative sizes or distances as the actual system. The scale model of the planets' orbits in Figure 5.6 uses a football field to show relative distances. In the model, the sun is placed at one goal line (0-yard line), and Neptune, the farthest planet from the sun, is placed at the other goal line 100 yards away.

The scale model shows that the first four planets are close together and close to the sun. These planets are all within 1.7 AU from the sun, and they are within 5 yards from the sun's goal line in the scale model. The last four planets in the solar system are between about 5.2 AU and 30 AU from the sun. Though the planet sizes are not on the same scale as the distances between planets, you can still see the distances between planets on Figure 5.6.

The football field model shows that the solar system has a lot of empty space between planets. If people did travel to another planet, it would have to travel a long distance between each planet.

Figure 5.6

This scale model uses two different scales for the size of the planets and the distances between them. If the solar system were scaled down to the size of a football field, the first four planets would fit within 5 yards from the sun. The last four planets would be spread out between 17 yards and 100 yards away.

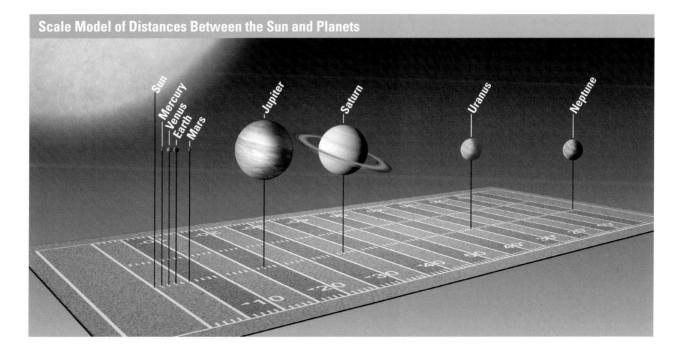

Scale Model of Distances Between the Sun and Planets

The Solar System

These two scale models of the solar system show the relative size (top) and the relative distance (bottom) between the planets. Gravitational forces between the massive sun and other objects in the solar system result in celestial objects revolving around the sun. Distances between celestial objects in space are very large and are often measured with a unit called the astronomical unit, which is equal to the average distance between the sun and Earth.

Comet

Outer Solar System

Inner Solar System

Sun

Planet Sizes Drawn to Scale

Asteroid belt

Average Distances Between the Sun and the Planets Drawn to Scale

Mars 1.5 AU
Earth 1 AU
Venus 0.7 AU
Mercury 0.4 AU
Sun 0 AU

Jupiter 5.2 AU

Saturn 9.6 AU

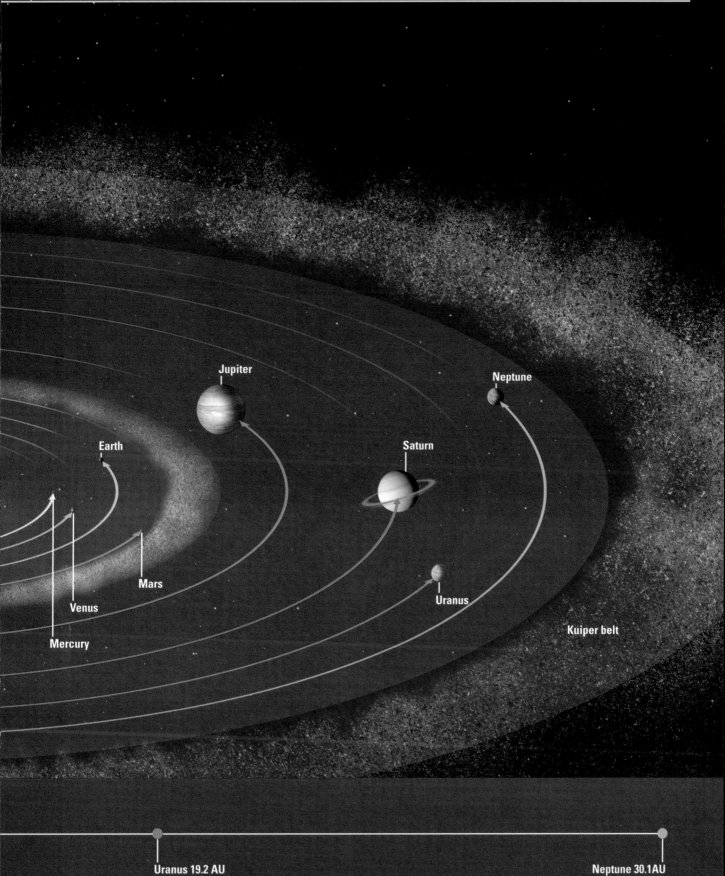

Jupiter

Neptune

Earth

Saturn

Venus

Mars

Uranus

Mercury

Kuiper belt

Uranus 19.2 AU

Neptune 30.1AU

7. Observing the Planets

All the planets are visible from Earth despite their far distances. You can see the planets because they reflect light from the sun. You just need to know when, where, and how to look for each planet. How can you observe the different planets?

Viewing Mercury and Venus Mercury is the closest planet to the sun, so it can be difficult to see. It is usually found near the sun in the sky. The sun is so bright that Mercury is usually hidden from view by the glare of the sun. However, on certain days, you can see Mercury low on the eastern horizon just before sunrise. On other days, you can see Mercury low on the western horizon just after sunset. Mercury is bright enough that you can see it with the unaided eye. However, if you view Mercury with a telescope, you will see that Mercury has phases similar to the moon's phases.

Unlike Mercury, Venus is very easy to spot even without a telescope. Like Mercury, Venus is very bright and can be seen at dawn and at dusk. It also has phases like Mercury.

Mercury and Venus have phases because the sun shines only on the half of each planet that is facing the sun. From Earth, different amounts of the lit half of Mercury and Venus can be seen depending on the planets' positions relative to the sun and Earth.

Viewing Mars, Jupiter, and Saturn Mars is very easy to see at night with the unaided eye. If you look carefully at Mars, you will notice that it has a reddish or orange color. Mars was named after the Roman god of war because of the planet's red color.

Although Jupiter is much farther away than Mars, it is also much bigger than Mars. So, Jupiter appears brighter than Mars. Jupiter can be seen with the unaided eye in the night sky. If you use a telescope to look at Jupiter, you might be able to see one or more of its moons. Four of Jupiter's moons are large enough to see with even a low-powered telescope.

Saturn is smaller and farther away than Jupiter, so it is dimmer than Jupiter. But Saturn is still bright enough to see at night with the unaided eye. If you look at Saturn with a telescope, you might be able to see its rings. You might also be able to see some of its moons.

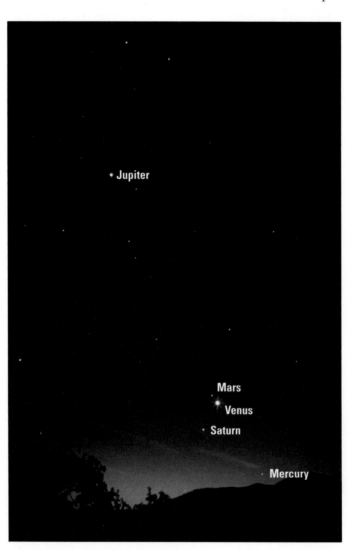

Many planets can be observed from Earth without tools. The brightest point of light in this photo is Venus. The next brightest spot is Jupiter. Mercury, Mars, and Saturn are also visible.

Viewing Uranus and Neptune Uranus is about 12 times smaller than Saturn, when Saturn is measured with its rings, and is also farther away than Saturn, making it appear very dim. Uranus is so dim that it is extremely hard to see with the unaided eye. To see it without tools, you have to go to a very dark location away from city lights on a clear and moonless night. You also need a star chart to know where to look. It is most easily seen using a telescope or binoculars.

Neptune is the farthest planet from the sun and is the only planet in the solar system that cannot be seen without tools. It is the hardest planet to see, not only because it is so dim, but also because it does not look very different from the stars. To see Neptune, you need a telescope or binoculars and a good star chart that tells you exactly where to look.

A good star chart is handy whenever you want to look at any of the planets. Star charts on mobile devices are particularly helpful because they will show you exactly where the planets are compared to the stars. So, on a clear night, grab a star chart and some binoculars, and take time to spy on the planets in Earth's neighborhood.

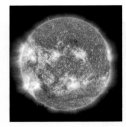

LESSON SUMMARY

Gravity and the Solar System

The Solar System and Gravitational Forces The solar system is held together by gravitational forces and is made up of the sun and all the objects that travel around it.

Earth Revolves Because of the Gravitational Force The gravitational force between Earth and the sun holds Earth in orbit because it acts nearly perpendicularly to the direction of Earth's motion.

The Planets The solar system has eight planets that directly revolve around the sun, are nearly spherical in shape, and have cleared the neighborhood around their orbits.

Moons Revolve Around Planets Moons directly revolve around planets and indirectly revolve around stars. Six planets in the solar system have moons revolving around them.

Dwarf Planets, Asteroids, and Comets Dwarf planets, asteroids, and comets have different characteristics and are all small objects that revolve around the sun.

Modeling Distances in the Solar System The solar system is so large that scientists often use a large unit of length, an astronomical unit, to discuss distances in the solar system. They also use scale models to show relative sizes and distances.

Observing the Planets Most planets in the solar system can be seen with the unaided eye. Using tools such as a telescope and a star chart will help you observe them.

Starman: Neil deGrasse Tyson

Neil deGrasse Tyson seems to be everywhere. In a viral video, he rolls on the floor while talking to a girl about science. On social networks, he rants about mistakes in science fiction movies. Photos of him wearing loud ties and vests featuring solar-system objects can be found all over the Internet. Just who IS Neil deGrasse Tyson?

Neil deGrasse Tyson is a celebrity. He is connected to several million people on social media. He has starred in multiple TV series and has his own podcast. He also makes live appearances in front of sold-out crowds. Tyson is not a movie actor or musician—he is an astrophysicist, a scientist who applies the laws and theories of physics and astronomy to study the universe and its contents.

Neil deGrasse Tyson became one of the most famous astrophysicists of his time, partly because of his social media presence. He is well-known as a celebrity and a scientist.

Tyson grew up in New York City, where light pollution overwhelms the light from most stars. Without a telescope, usually only the moon, a few planets, and the brightest stars can be seen at night there. As a young child, Tyson had never seen the sky filled with stars and other celestial objects. But that changed at the age of nine when he visited the Hayden Planetarium and had the first of many experiences that led him to decide that he wanted to be an astrophysicist. As he grew up, he thought about the stars and space almost all the time.

Tyson was not the best-behaved student in school. He preferred to spend class time socializing instead of doing work. But his sixth grade teacher noticed his interest in astronomy and suggested he take a class at the Hayden Planetarium. The class was supposed to be for older students, but Tyson loved it and learned that the planetarium was a great place for him to feed his interest in astronomy. Tyson continued to take classes at the planetarium throughout middle school and high school. Some of the classes were advanced science classes intended for college students and adults. Tyson's education outside of school was as important as his education in school.

Astronomical Adventures

Tyson's love for astronomy led him to some extraordinary experiences. For example, when he was 14, he got a scholarship to go alone on a science-study cruise to the coast of Africa to see a solar eclipse. He was the youngest person traveling alone on the cruise, and when asked about his age, he exaggerated and said that he was 16. He traveled alongside thousands of scientists and amateur astronomers who wanted to see and study the eclipse. Tyson felt like a true astronomer himself as he watched the eclipse, gazed at star-filled skies, listened to scientists' speeches, and delivered the winning answer in an astronomy trivia contest!

Astronomy might also be blamed for several encounters Tyson had with the police. As a teenager, Tyson saved up enough money to buy a large telescope—so large that it looked like a miniature cannon. Because he lived in a big city, the best place for him to set up the telescope was the roof of his apartment building. It must have looked dangerous to neighbors who saw the silhouette of what looked like a cannon on the roof of a nearby building. The police were called many times to investigate what he was doing. However, Tyson was always able to impress the police by encouraging them to gaze at the moon or the stars through his telescope.

Tyson lived in New York City, where the city lights overwhelm the light from the stars. To help see the stars, Tyson would put a telescope on the roof of his apartment building.

Serious Space Studies

After high school, Tyson attended Harvard University to begin his formal education in astrophysics. At Harvard, he naturally enrolled in a lot of science classes in astronomy and physics, but he also took classes in art and design. He studied hard but also had interests outside of the sciences. Tyson was an athlete and became a member of Harvard's rowing and wrestling teams. He also a danced in Harvard's Expressions Dance Company.

Tyson graduated from Harvard in 1980 and continued his education in graduate school at the University of Texas at Austin and at Columbia University. In graduate school, Tyson spent years researching dwarf galaxies. A *galaxy* is a collection of stars, dust, and gases, and like the solar system, they are held together by gravitational forces. A *dwarf galaxy* is a galaxy that is smaller and fainter than other galaxies. Tyson wrote papers about his research that were published in well-respected science journals. Tyson had finally become a professional astrophysicist.

Around the same time that Tyson was writing complex papers for scientists to read, he started writing astronomy articles for nonscientists. Through this writing, Tyson shared the excitement and amazement of space. Teaching the general public about the wonders of astronomy and other areas of science became a new mission for Tyson.

Tyson devoted much of his time to his passion: astrophysics. He was present at the 2011 ribbon-cutting ceremony for Southern Illinois University's new observatory, which is used by astrophysics students for their research.

Tyson's excitement for science and dynamic speaking style inspired many people to be curious about science.

Back to the Beginning

In 1994, after graduating from Texas and Columbia, Tyson went back to the Hayden Planetarium. When people visit a planetarium, they go to observe star shows or look at museum-like exhibits. But that was not what Tyson did when he went back to Hayden. Instead, he went to the planetarium to work as a staff scientist and developed the shows and displays that teach visitors about astronomy. Before long, he became the director of the very place where he first became interested in astrophysics.

Through his work at the Hayden Planetarium and his writing, Tyson became an advocate for science education and science research. An *advocate* is someone who speaks out in support of something. Tyson was a confident speaker and did an excellent job explaining science concepts. He was invited to give talks all over the country and was hired to be the host of the science TV show *NOVA Science Now*.

Tyson's fame in the science world and in the entertainment world grew. He made guest appearances on talk shows and TV programs, such as *The Big Bang Theory* and *Stargate: Atlantis*. At the same time, his social media popularity exploded.

Tyson will long be known for his passion for astronomy, his deep scientific knowledge, and his ability to make the science of the stars exciting and entertaining. He has encouraged many young people to be curious and follow their passions. He followed his passion and became a superstar in the process. ◆

Tyson became so famous that he was invited to the White House to watch student-made films about technology in schools. While he was there, he and fellow science celebrity Bill Nye took a selfie with President Obama.

The Inner Solar System

What are the characteristics of the terrestrial planets?

Introduction

"Make a wish!" Wishing on the evening star is an old superstition. Many songs and poems promise that wishes made on the evening star will come true. But did you know that the evening star is not a star at all? The object in the sky that is commonly called the evening star is actually the planet Venus. Venus is one of four planets found in the inner solar system.

How is Venus similar to or different from the other planets in the inner solar system? Previously, you learned how gravity holds all of the solar system together. Now, you will explore the inner solar system, which includes the four planets Mercury, Venus, Earth and Mars. At the edge of the inner solar system is the asteroid belt and dwarf planet Ceres.

Scientists use models to study the solar system. Because the solar system is so large, models like this orrery, shown in the photo, were invented to help people understand attributes of the solar system. However, these models cannot show every aspect of the inner solar system.

As you learn about the components of the inner solar system, you will analyze and interpret data about the different planets to identify their similarities and differences. These similarities allow the planets to be classified as the inner solar system planets. The distinct characteristics of each planet result in different challenges when trying to explore their surfaces.

Vocabulary

ground-based telescope a telescope that is placed on Earth's surface

space telescope a telescope that is located in outer space

data information collected that can be used to support explanations

terrestrial planet a planet that has a hard, rocky surface

orbital radius the average distance at which the planet revolves around the sun

planetary radius the distance from the center of the planet's core to the outer edge of its atmosphere

Next Generation Science Standards

Performance Expectations

MS-ESS1-3. Analyze and interpret data to determine scale properties of objects in the solar system.

MS-ETS1-2. Evaluate competing design solutions using a systematic process to determine how well they meet the criteria and constraints of the problem.

Science and Engineering Practices

Analyzing and Interpreting Data Analyze and interpret data to determine similarities and differences in findings.

Engaging in Argument from Evidence Evaluate competing design solutions based on jointly developed and agreed-upon design criteria.

Crosscutting Concepts

Scale, Proportion, and Quantity Time, space, and energy phenomena can be observed at various scales using models to study systems that are too large or too small.

Interdependence of Science, Engineering, and Technology

Disciplinary Core Ideas

ESS1.B. The solar system consists of the sun and a collection of objects, including planets, their moons, and asteroids that are held in orbit around the sun by its gravitational pull on them.

ETS1.B. There are systematic processes for evaluating solutions with respect to how well they meet the criteria and constraints of a problem.

1. Technology Improves Observations of the Solar System

If you had a bike, you might use it to ride five kilometers in a day. If you rode in a car, you could travel a thousand kilometers in a day. How far you can travel depends on the technology that you use. Technology has a similar effect in astronomy. Scientists can see farther into space and learn more about it by using more advanced technology.

The Unaided Eye Ancient astronomers had only their eyes to look at celestial objects. Yet, they were able to make accurate observations. They noticed that a few very bright points of light moved differently from other points of light in the sky. Stars appear to stay in the same positions relative to each other. But planets move around relative to the stars. The planets known to ancient astronomers were Mercury, Venus, Mars, Jupiter, and Saturn. Dimmer objects, such as the moons of other planets and far away stars, could not be seen.

Ground-Based Telescopes Telescopes are tools that collect light and concentrate it for better observation. A **ground-based telescope** is a telescope that is placed on Earth's surface. One of the first ground-based telescopes was built by Italian astronomer Galileo Galilei. He used this telescope to look closely at the sun, the moon, and the planets in 1609 and 1610. He was the first person to see that Venus has phases and Jupiter has moons.

Since Galileo's time, scientists have been improving telescopes. In 1668, Isaac Newton built the first telescope that used a curved mirror to collect light. In the 1850's, scientists added a thin layer of silver on telescope mirrors to allow them to see far away objects more clearly. Today, scientists use large, powerful telescopes to study dim and far away objects.

GALILEO.

Galileo built one of the first ground-based telescopes. Scientists still use ground-based telescopes today, but the telescopes that they use are much larger than the one Galileo used.

Space Telescopes Large ground-based telescopes are very powerful, but they have some limits. They can only collect light that travels through Earth's atmosphere. Earth's atmosphere blocks some light and makes objects look blurry. Light pollution from Earth can also interfere. To avoid these problems, scientists and engineers put telescopes in space. **Space telescopes** are telescopes that are located in outer space.

The Hubble Space Telescope is a famous space telescope. Astronomers used the Hubble Telescope to observe things that had never been seen before—discovering moons of dwarf planets, observing a comet hitting Jupiter, and finding solar systems forming around young stars.

Spacecraft Astronomers can learn a lot using telescopes, but they can learn much more by getting close to celestial objects. Since the late 1950s, astronomers have sent spacecraft to different parts of the solar system. Some spacecraft fly by or revolve around a celestial object, while others land on it. Since spacecraft can fly very close to celestial objects, they can take more detailed photos and obtain specific data about the celestial objects' structures. **Data** is information collected that can be used to support explanations. Many spacecraft carried cameras and tools to take images and collect data about the atmosphere and surfaces of planets and moons.

Astronomical Technology Leads to New Products A lot of technology has been developed for improving astronomical observations. But the use of that technology has not been limited to astronomy. Water filters in swimming pools, digital cameras, shoe insoles, and invisible braces for teeth are all everyday objects that were invented thanks to technology developed for space exploration.

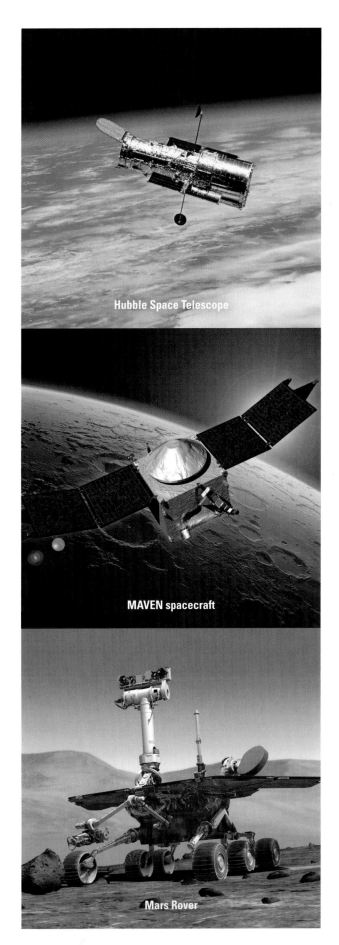

Hubble Space Telescope

MAVEN spacecraft

Mars Rover

The Hubble Telescope, the spacecraft MAVEN, and the Mars Rover have all led to better understanding of the solar system.

2. Key Characteristics of the Terrestrial Planets

If you were playing basketball on the moon, then you would be able to leap higher than if you were playing on Earth. What if you were playing basketball on the other planets? How are they different from Earth?

Structure and Mass of the Planets Mercury, Venus, Earth, and Mars are found in the inner solar system. Each of these planets is a **terrestrial planet,** or a planet that has a hard, rocky surface. Like Earth, the other terrestrial planets have mountains, valleys, and large flat plains.

The terrestrial planets also have a similar internal structure, as shown by Figure 6.2A. The center of each planet is a metal core. The core is surrounded by the mantle, which is made of rock. Around the mantle is the crust. The crust is also made of rock. When you read about the surface of a planet, you are learning about the crust. While all terrestrial planets have a core, mantle, and crust, the thicknesses of each layer varies from planet to planet.

Above each terrestrial planet's crust is its atmosphere. The thickness of a terrestrial planet's atmosphere is related to its mass. Planets that have larger masses usually have thicker atmospheres because gravity holds more gas near the planet.

Earth, for example, has more mass than Mars has. As shown by Figure 6.2B, the gravitational forces that pull matter toward Earth are stronger than the gravitational forces that pull matter toward Mercury. The stronger gravitational forces are able to hold more gases around Earth to form a thicker atmosphere.

Figure 6.2A

Terrestrial planets have a hard, rocky surface called a crust. They also contain a core made of metal and a mantle made of rock that lies between the crust and core. This scale model compares the relative sizes of the terrestrial planet's crust, mantle, and core.

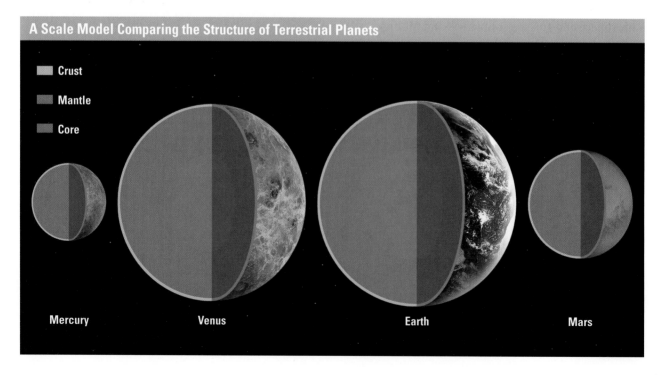

A Scale Model Comparing the Structure of Terrestrial Planets

■ Crust
■ Mantle
■ Core

Mercury   Venus   Earth   Mars

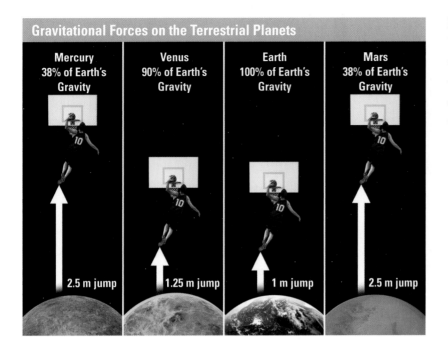

Gravitational Forces on the Terrestrial Planets

Mercury 38% of Earth's Gravity	Venus 90% of Earth's Gravity	Earth 100% of Earth's Gravity	Mars 38% of Earth's Gravity
2.5 m jump	1.25 m jump	1 m jump	2.5 m jump

Figure 6.2B
The other terrestrial planets have weaker gravitational forces because they have smaller masses. As a result, you could jump higher on those planets than you could on Earth.

Orbital Characteristics All the planets trace nearly circular orbits around the sun, but each planet is located a different distance from the sun. The average distance at which a planet revolves around the sun is called its **orbital radius**. Of the terrestrial planets, Mercury is the closest to the sun and Mars is the farthest. The greater the distance between a planet and the sun, the larger the planet's orbital radius is. As Mars travels around the sun, it traces a bigger ellipse than Mercury does. So Mars has to travel farther than Mercury does to revolve around the sun once.

Although the planets revolve at different distances from the sun, they all revolve in the same direction. If you could look down from above the orbital planes of the planets, you would see that the planets revolve in a counterclockwise direction. Like Earth, as each planet revolves, it also rotates on its axis. However, each planet rotates at a different speed, and each planet's axis is tilted by a different amount.

Surface Characteristics In general, planets that are closer to the sun are warmer than planets that are farther away. This is because surface temperature depends on the concentration of sunlight that hits the planet. Planets closer to the sun receive more concentrated sunlight than planets farther away do. But the surface temperature of a particular planet depends on many things. For example, surface temperature also depends on a planet's atmosphere. Thick atmospheres can hold more thermal energy than thin atmospheres can.

As a group, the terrestrial planets are similar to each other. They all have a similar structure, and they all revolve and rotate. But the terrestrial planets do differ from each other in various ways. Their planetary radii and orbital radii are different lengths, and their surface temperatures and features are not the same.

3. Mercury

Mercury is a planet of extremes. It is the closest planet to the sun and the smallest planet in our solar system. As you learned, it is difficult to see from Earth because it is always so close to the sun in the sky. So, much of what is known about Mercury has come from NASA spacecraft sent to Mercury in 1973 and 2004: Mariner 10 and MESSENGER.

Mercury's Radius and Mass Mercury is the smallest planet in the solar system in planetary radius and mass. A planet's **planetary radius** is the distance from the center of its core to the outer edge of its atmosphere. The core makes up about 80 percent of Mercury's radius, which is a higher proportion than any other planet. Mercury's small mass also means that the gravitational force between it and other objects is weak. So, its gravity does not hold gases around the planet very well. As a result, Mercury's atmosphere is very thin.

Mercury's Orbital Characteristics Mercury's orbital radius is about 0.4 AU. Mercury travels quickly around its short orbit, so it only needs 88 Earth days to revolve once around the sun.

However, Mercury rotates very slowly. A day is the amount of time needed for a planet to rotate once on its axis. The length of a day on Mercury is almost 59 Earth days. That means that a Mercury year is about one and a half Mercury days long!

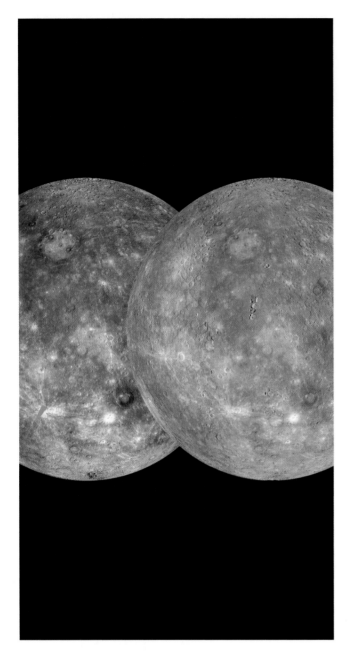

Scientists used cameras on spacecraft revolving around Mercury to take photos of the planet's surface. This photo shows two different sides of Mercury on top of each other. The whole planet is covered in craters.

Mercury's Surface Characteristics Unsurprisingly, Mercury is very hot. But, surprisingly, Mercury is also very cold. The side of the planet that faces the sun (the day side) can reach temperatures of more than 420°C, which is as hot as a pizza oven. However, the side that faces away from the sun (the night side) can be as cold as –170°C, which is almost as cold as liquid nitrogen. This is because Mercury's thin atmosphere does not retain thermal energy. In fact, scientists using telescopes discovered that parts of Mercury stay cold enough that ice could stay frozen there!

Mercury's surface looks similar to the moon's surface. It is covered with craters where the planet was hit by meteorites. Mercury's Caloris Basin is a huge crater formed when a large asteroid-sized object hit the planet. It is one of the solar system's largest craters.

This photo of Venus's surface was taken by a Soviet spacecraft that landed on Venus in 1982. The photo shows that Venus's surface is dry and rocky.

4. Venus

The first successful spacecraft mission to another planet was the Mariner 2 mission to Venus. Mariner 2 flew by Venus in 1962 and took data for 42 minutes. That may not seem like a very long time to you, but some surprising things were learned about the planet Venus from that mission.

Venus's Radius and Mass Venus is the second largest terrestrial planet and is similar to Earth in both planetary radius and mass. Venus's mass results in gravitational forces strong enough to hold onto a thick atmosphere around its surface. The Mariner 2 mission discovered that Venus has a dense atmosphere filled with thick clouds. A later mission to Venus showed that, instead of water, many of the clouds were made of acid!

Venus's Orbital Characteristics Venus has an orbital radius of about 0.7 AU. Like Mercury, Venus travels quickly. A year on Venus is only about 225 Earth days long.

One of the most interesting things learned by Mariner 2 was that Venus rotates backward from most of the other planets. On most planets, the sun rises toward the east and sets toward the west. However, on Venus, the sun rises toward the west and sets toward the east. Like Mercury, Venus rotates very slowly. A day on Venus is 243 Earth days long. So, a day on Venus is longer than a year on Venus!

Venus's Surface Characteristics In general, you expect planets closer to the sun to be hotter. However, Venus actually has higher temperatures than the day side of Mercury. It has temperatures greater than 460°C. These higher temperatures happen because Venus's thick atmosphere absorbs and traps thermal energy from the sun. This is called the greenhouse effect and is the same effect that occurs on Earth.

Venus's surface has features similar to Earth. It has mountains, valleys, and young volcanoes. Scientists estimate that Venus was completely covered in lava from volcanoes 300–500 million years ago.

This photo of Venus shows the clouds in its atmosphere. Unlike clouds on Earth, which are made of water, Venus's clouds are made of acid.

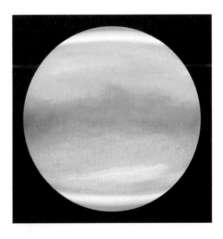

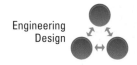

5. Designing a Venus Rover

Venus is our nearest neighbor in the solar system, and yet it is the most mysterious of the planets in the inner solar system. Because thick clouds always cover Venus, people cannot easily see Venus's surface. With a thick atmosphere full of sulfuric acid, temperatures that can be greater than 460°C, and atmospheric pressure around 90 times higher than Earth's, Venus's surface is exceptionally difficult to explore. Despite these challenges, NASA engineers have worked together to consider different designs for rovers, machines that explore planet surfaces. These rovers will not only be able to land on Venus, but also will be able to explore its surface and gather scientific data in several different locations.

The Mission's Criteria and Constraints There are many problems engineers must solve when designing a rover that will be sent to another planet. The engineers face major constraints. First, they have a limited budget. Second, it can't weigh too much since heavy objects require more fuel, and thus are very expensive to launch into space. Engineers also have many criteria, which they strive to meet. The rover should be as simple as possible because a complex design has many more things that could go wrong and prevent the rover from working properly. In addition, a rover going to Venus needs to be able to operate on Venus's surface.

This computer generated image of Venus's surface was created using the probes that mapped most of Venus's surface. With high temperatures and atmospheric pressure, engineers had to design a rover that could withstand a harsh environment.

Comparing Two Rover Designs NASA engineers proposed two designs for rovers that would be able to explore the surface of Venus. Both designs meet many of the criteria for the mission, but neither one is a perfect solution.

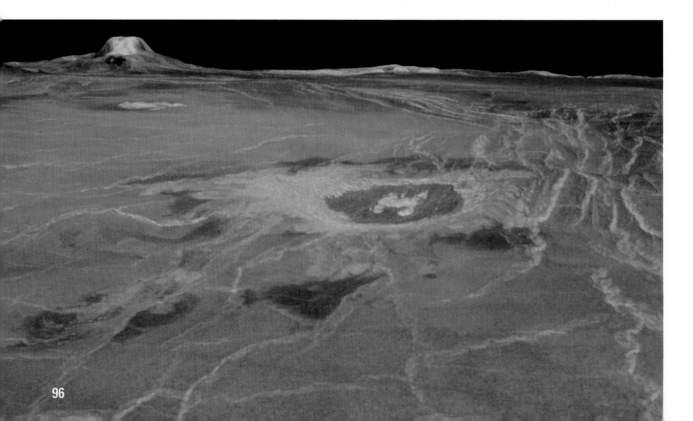

This illustration by NASA shows that the sail boat design would have a sail over 4 m tall. This is even taller than a basketball hoop. This rover design is very light, but the large sail would make it difficult to send to Venus. Also it could easily be blown over by the wind.

The first design was inspired by a sail boat. It uses a large sail to catch the wind and roll the rover around the surface. The wind on Venus is not very strong, but the atmosphere is so dense that even a light breeze would be enough to push the rover across the surface. The sail and the top of the rover would be covered in solar panels to generate electricity for the rover's scientific instruments. This design has several advantages. It is very simple and does not have many moving parts, so it is hard for parts to malfunction. It is also very light. However, the mast holding the sail would have to be over 4 meters tall, which is taller than a basketball hoop! The sail would be difficult to fit into the landing vehicle. Additionally, scientists would not be able to precisely control where the rover moves using the sail. The rover might also be knocked over by a strong gust of wind.

The second design uses a wind turbine (like that found on a windmill) to generate electricity. The electricity powers the scientific instruments and also produces enough power to run motors which drive each of the rover's wheels. This design avoids several of the disadvantages of the sail-based design. Directly controlling the wheels with motors allows the engineers precise control over where the rover moves. It is also much easier to fit into the landing vehicle. Additionally, it is able to use higher wind speeds to charge faster, rather than being at risk of tipping over. However, it is a much more complex design. The additional moving parts are at risk of breaking, causing the mission to fail. It also would weigh more than the other design, making it more expensive to launch from Earth. Finally, if the wind dies down, it could take the rover Earth days or even weeks to charge its batteries.

Choosing a Design The engineers calculated the designs' effectiveness to decide which one was more likely to successfully complete the mission they had in mind. Based on their comparison of the two designs, the engineers decided that the design using a wind turbine was less risky and more likely to be able to successfully complete its mission.

6. Earth and the Moon

Earth and the moon are the only two objects in the solar system that humans have stood on. Thus, more is known about Earth and the moon than most other celestial objects.

Earth's Radius and Mass Earth is the largest of the terrestrial planets. Earth's crust is less than 1 percent of its planetary radius. Earth has an atmosphere that you and other living things breathe. This atmosphere is held around the planet in large part because Earth's large mass results in a strong gravitational force.

Earth's Orbital Characteristics Earth's orbital radius is, on average, 1 AU. The length of Earth's orbit is 9.4×10^8 km. Earth takes about 365 days to revolve around the sun once. You call this length of time a year, but it is more precisely an *Earth year*.

Earth rotates on its tilted axis once every 24 hours, which is the length of time called an Earth day. The length of other planets' days and years are usually given in comparison to Earth days and Earth years.

This photo, called Earthrise, is one of the most famous photos taken by a person in orbit around the moon. It was taken during the Apollo 8 mission in 1968. From space, Earth looks mostly blue because of all the water on the planet's surface. The white swirls are clouds in the atmosphere surrounding the planet.

Earth's Surface Characteristics If you listen to a weather report, you know that Earth's surface temperature varies from place to place. Temperature also varies with the seasons. However, on Earth, temperatures range from about −90°C to 60°C. Earth's temperature range is important because it allows liquid water to exist on the planet's surface. Liquid water is thought to be necessary for life.

The Moon Many spacecraft have been sent to the moon because it is much closer to Earth than any other celestial object. People even visited the moon in the 1960s and 1970s during the Apollo missions. Through data gathered by the many moon missions, the moon's entire surface has been mapped. Scientists' knowledge of the moon and Earth are used to interpret data gathered from other planets and celestial objects.

Mars's surface is dry and rocky, and it is reddish in color. Its red surface makes Mars look red, even when viewed from Earth with the unaided eye.

7. Mars

Would you like to go to Mars? Quite a bit of information about Mars has been gathered by various spacecraft. From the data, scientists think people could live on Mars, but it would not be easy.

Mars's Mass Mars is the second smallest planet in the solar system. It's about half the size of Earth. So, Mars's crust is thick relative to its size. Mars's small mass also means that gravity that holds the planet's atmosphere is not very strong. As a result, Mars has a thin atmosphere. The atmosphere is too thin and does not contain enough oxygen for a person to breathe.

Mars's Orbital Characteristics Mars is 1.5 AU from the sun. Mars travels slower and farther in its orbit than Earth does, which makes a year on Mars about 687 Earth days. Like Earth, Mars is tilted on its axis. So, as Mars revolves around the sun, it has seasons similar to the seasons on Earth. Furthermore, Mars rotates at almost the same speed as Earth. One Mars day is 24 hours and 39 minutes long.

Mars's Surface Characteristics In general, the surface temperatures on Mars are lower than the temperatures on Earth because Mars is farther away from the sun and because it has a thinner atmosphere. Mars's temperature ranges from about –150°C to 20°C. The lower end of that range is much colder than dry ice, which is used when transporting ice cream cakes to keep them frozen, and the upper end is about the temperature of an air-conditioned room.

Because the temperature on Mars can be above water's freezing point, liquid water flows seasonally. Many spacecraft mission to Mars have sent back data that show that Mars once had rivers and lakes. In 2015, scientists discovered that liquid water flows intermittently on present-day Mars.

Without plentiful liquid water or oxygen, Mars is not the best place for people to live. But its temperatures would be bearable. If people did want to live on another planet, Mars may well be the best choice.

Several spacecraft have visited Mars. Some spacecraft revolved around the planet, and some landed on its surface.

Model of the Inner Solar System

The inner solar system is composed of terrestrial planets and the asteroid belt, which includes one dwarf planet. Planets can be described by their atmosphere, their relative crustal thickness, orbital characteristics, and surface characteristics. This image models the planets of the inner solar system and the asteroid belt. The chart compiles data on the terrestrial planets.

Mars
Mars has a thin atmosphere. However, the planet has enough air around it to have clouds, fog, and wind. Mars, like Earth, has liquid water on its surface. Mars has two very small moons. At this scale, they are as small as tiny specks.

Mars

Asteroid Belt
The asteroid belt is a doughnut-shaped region between 2 and 4 AU away from the sun. Though it contains many asteroids, they are all very spread apart. The average distance between two asteroids is more than 1–3 million km, so most of the asteroid belt is empty space.

Mercury

Mercury is the closest planet to the sun. It has very little atmosphere and rotates very slowly. As a result, the day side of Mercury has very high temperatures, and the night side has very low temperatures.

Venus

Although Venus is the second closest planet to the sun, it has the highest temperatures. Venus's temperatures are so high because its dense atmosphere and thick clouds trap thermal energy from the sun. Venus is the only terrestrial planet that rotates from west to east.

Earth

Earth is one of the planets that has liquid water on its surface and is the only object in the solar system known to have life on it. Earth has one moon, called *the moon*.

Sun

Mercury

Venus

Earth

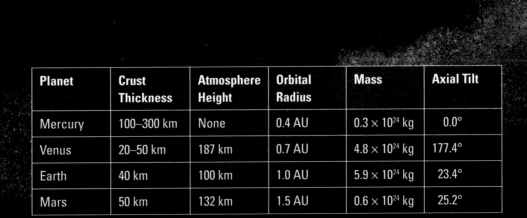

Planet	Crust Thickness	Atmosphere Height	Orbital Radius	Mass	Axial Tilt
Mercury	100–300 km	None	0.4 AU	0.3×10^{24} kg	0.0°
Venus	20–50 km	187 km	0.7 AU	4.8×10^{24} kg	177.4°
Earth	40 km	100 km	1.0 AU	5.9×10^{24} kg	23.4°
Mars	50 km	132 km	1.5 AU	0.6×10^{24} kg	25.2°

8. The Asteroid Belt and Ceres

In science fiction movies, you sometimes see a spacecraft trying to fly through an asteroid field. The asteroids are so close together that the spacecraft has to swerve constantly to avoid being hit. It looks exciting, but it is not true to life.

The Asteroid Belt The asteroid belt lies outside of Mars's orbit. It makes up a doughnut-shaped region between about 2 and 4 AU from the sun. The asteroid belt contains millions of asteroids, and the asteroids are very far apart. The average distance between any two asteroids is more than 1 million km. That is far enough apart that a spacecraft would not have to make fast movements to avoid them.

Asteroids vary in size and shape. They range from less than 1 km across to more than 570 km across (about the distance between Chicago and Minneapolis). They are rocky and usually have irregular shapes.

Several spacecraft have studied asteroids up close. In 1997, the NEAR Shoemaker spacecraft flew by an asteroid. In 1998, it began revolving around a second asteroid called Eros. Then, three years later, NEAR landed on Eros. NEAR discovered that Eros was a solid object made of one kind of rock. It is not made of a variety of different rocks mashed together like Earth is. NEAR took photos of many other asteroids, showing that asteroids have craters, large boulders, and debris on their surfaces.

Ceres is the largest object in the asteroid belt and is a dwarf planet. The Dawn spacecraft reached orbit around Ceres in 2015 and astronomers will use the data it collects to learn more about Ceres and how planets, dwarf planets, and asteroids form.

21 Lutetia

253 Mathilde

243 Ida/1 Dactyl

433 Eros

951 Gaspra

2867 Šteins

5535 Annefrank

25143 Itokawa

4 Vesta

Most of the asteroids in the solar system are found in the asteroid belt. But some asteroids are not. Some asteroids cross the orbits of planets, including Earth's orbit. Scientists keep track of all asteroids that cross Earth's orbit to predict if they are likely to hit Earth.

Ceres The largest object in the asteroid belt is a dwarf planet called Ceres. Ceres is about 950 km across, which makes it much larger than anything else in the asteroid belt. However, it is the tiniest dwarf planet known. Ceres is also the only dwarf planet in the asteroid belt.

Scientists saw plumes of water vapor shooting out from Ceres's surface, and they think that Ceres has a layer under its crust that is made of ice. Earth has water and ice above its crust. If scientists are right, Ceres could have as much fresh water as Earth does on its surface. However, it is all frozen and is mostly trapped under the dwarf planet's rock crust.

Ceres is the largest object in the asteroid belt and is a dwarf planet.

LESSON SUMMARY

The Inner Solar System

Technology Improves Observations of the Solar System Increasingly advanced technology has allowed astronomers to learn more about the solar system and space.

Key Characteristics of the Terrestrial Planets The terrestrial planets have rocky crusts and metallic cores. The thickness of each planet's atmosphere depends primarily on each planet's gravitational force.

Mercury Mercury is the closest planet to the sun, the smallest planet in the solar system, and has extremely hot daytime temperatures and extremely cold nighttime temperatures.

Venus Venus is the second planet from the sun and has a dense atmosphere, which traps thermal energy from the sun.

Designing a Venus Rover Engineers had to develop a system to carefully evaluate different design solutions to see how well they addressed the criteria and constraints for a Venus rover that could survive on Venus's dangerous surface.

Earth and the Moon Earth is the third planet from the sun and is the only planet that has persistent liquid water on its surface. More is known about Earth and the moon than most other celestial objects.

Mars Mars is the fourth planet from the sun, is the last terrestrial planet, and has liquid water that flows seasonally on its surface.

The Asteroid Belt and Ceres Ceres is the largest object in the asteroid belt, which is a region in the solar system between Mars and Jupiter that contains more than a million small rocky objects.

The Out-of-This-World Adventures of Curiosity

On August 5, 2012, NASA scientists and engineers waited anxiously for a signal from Mars. No, they weren't expecting to hear from aliens living on Mars! They were waiting find out if the robotic rover Curiosity had arrived safely on the planet's surface. How did Curiosity get to Mars, and what was it doing there?

After traveling more than eight months, Curiosity landed on Mars. This drawing shows how the sky crane lowered Curiosity to Mars's surface.

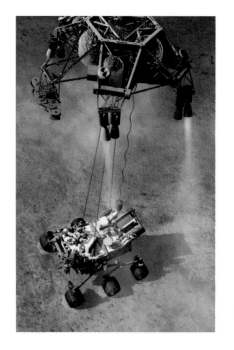

A Quiet Voyage, Then a Landing in Stages

Curiosity landed on Mars a little more than eight months after it was launched from Earth. Most of that trip was uneventful. However, as Curiosity entered Mars's atmosphere, the people at NASA became more and more nervous. Although other spacecraft had successfully landed on the planet, the rover Curiosity was bigger and heavier than any craft that had come before it. People did not know what would happen.

Curiosity's landing involved several stages. To ensure a safe landing, Curiosity traveled through most of Mars's atmosphere inside a capsule. The bottom of the capsule was a heat shield, and the top contained a parachute that opened when Curiosity was about 11 km from the ground. The parachute slowed its fall until it was about 1.6 km from the ground. At that point, Curiosity and an attached "sky crane" separated from the capsule. The sky crane had retrorockets, which are rockets that fire downward to slow the spacecraft even more. When Curiosity was about 20 m above the ground, the sky crane gently lowered it to the ground on long cables. Once Curiosity touched down, the cables broke away, and the sky crane flew off to crash away from Curiosity.

NASA scientists and engineers held their breath as they followed the landing on their instruments at the control center in Pasadena, California. Mars is too far away for people on Earth to guide a spacecraft there in real time, so the entire sequence had to be done automatically by the computers in the spacecraft. When Curiosity finally sent its first signal from Mars, the people waiting at NASA and all around the world cheered. Curiosity was safe and ready to begin its long mission on Mars.

A Roaming Robot Researcher

Engineers designed Curiosity's parts quite appropriately for a robot with a curious nature. The parts seemed part-human, part-car. All the parts were controlled by a computer that acted as Curiosity's "brain." Curiosity was the size of a large car and had six wheels, which allowed the rover to move easily over rocks and uneven ground. How would Curiosity know where it was going? Curiosity needed "eyes" to see where it was going and what it was doing. To solve this problem, engineers placed 17 cameras all over the rover so that it could see in many directions at once.

Just as humans do more than look around and move, so did Curiosity. It was designed as a robotic science lab to help scientists determine if humans could live on Mars. Scientists wondered: what would humans need to do in order to survive in Mars's environment? The rover gathered samples from Mars's crust with its robotic arm and hand to study its geology and atmosphere. The arm extended to reach objects, and the hand had instruments that could test the samples. The instruments were designed to look for hydrogen, oxygen, nitrogen, and substances containing carbon. These elements are important for humans to live; also, they are often found in the substances that make up the living things on Earth. The instruments took the samples and separated them into individual substances. Then, the substances were analyzed to determine their identities.

Curiosity's radio antennas were used to receive information from Earth. They were also used to send information to the scientists and engineers studying Mars. The people on Earth told the rover what to do, and the rover sent photos and data back to Earth. Of course, the distance between Earth and Mars meant that scientists could not control Curiosity in "real time." Instead, they sent a command to the rover, which carried out the command several minutes later. The scientists then waited for Curiosity to collect and send data back, which took many more minutes to arrive at Earth. Curiosity sent back a huge amount of information about Mars's geology and atmosphere to help determine if humans could live on Mars.

Curiosity, as large as an automobile, was designed to have parts similar to some human body parts. Its large robotic arm was designed to collect and analyze samples.

Are We Alone?

In some of the most spine-tingling science fiction movies, Earth is visited—or attacked—by aliens from other planets. Scientists have not yet found evidence of life on other planets, but that's not stopping them from looking. They are asking questions that will help them determine if there is life or evidence of past life on Mars.

Scientists do not think that Mars ever had life forms such as humans or even plants, but they think that bacteria-like organisms may have lived or are living on Mars. To determine if life existed on Mars, Curiosity looked for substances called *organic compounds*. Organic compounds contain the element carbon and are found in all living things on Earth. Scientists were excited but cautious when Curiosity found organic compounds within the rocks and soil on Mars. The scientists were cautious because they did not know if the substances were originally from Mars. A meteorite could have deposited them from elsewhere in the solar system, or the rover itself could have brought the substances to Mars from Earth.

One of Curiosity's most interesting discoveries was the detection of a sudden, temporary increase in an organic compound called *methane* in Mars's atmosphere. Methane can be a sign of life; on Earth, certain types of microorganisms produce methane. However, methane can also be produced in other ways. For example, a chemical reaction between water and a type of mineral called *olivine* can produce methane. As a result, scientists could not say for sure that Mars had life. Yet, finding the methane was important because it was an organic compound on Mars.

Curiosity also looked for signs of water, which is thought to be necessary for life. When the rover reported that it had found a dried up creek bed, a dried up lake, and sedimentary rock layers, the scientists had evidence that water once flowed on the surface of Mars. Sedimentary rock forms when grains of sand and other sediment are compressed, a process that often happens underwater. Analysis of the rock showed that it did not contain very much salt, which means that the water could have been fresh, drinkable water.

These hints that life may exist or may have existed on Mars may not seem like strong evidence. But it's enough to say, outside of science fiction, "we might not be alone in the universe."

Curiosity gathered information that could help scientists determine if life exists or existed on Mars. The rover took this photo of sedimentary rock layers on Mars. This type of rock forms underwater, which means that water must have once flowed on Mars's surface.

Another Giant Leap for Humankind?

In science fiction movies and television shows, people travel across space to different planets. In reality, the farthest that humans have traveled is the moon, and the last time people stood on the moon was in 1972. Why haven't people traveled to another planet?

Of the planets in the solar system, people could only visit the terrestrial planets because they have surfaces to land on. Mars is the most logical planet to visit first because it is close to Earth. (Venus is closer, but its atmosphere and temperatures are too dangerous for humans.) Yet, sending people to Mars will be very difficult.

The shortest travel time to Mars is more than half a year, and this short travel time can only be done when Earth and Mars are in certain positions in their orbits around the sun. Travelers to Mars would then have to leave the planet a few weeks after arriving if they wanted to have a similarly short travel time back. So, an entire trip would last more than a year, with little time for exploring Mars.

A crewed mission to Mars will be difficult and will not likely happen anytime soon. For now, robot rovers such as Curiosity will have to be the primary explorers of the planet.

Whatever spacecraft took humans to Mars would need to carry a large amount of food, water, oxygen, and fuel. As a result, the spacecraft carrying people to Mars would have to be very large and heavy. Launching, steering, and landing such a large spacecraft will be a challenge for engineers.

The Curiosity mission and other missions to Mars allow engineers to design and test different ways to travel to and land on the planet. These designs may lead to a design for a crewed spacecraft that can land on and take off from Mars.

Keeping people safe on Mars will also be difficult because the planet has very high levels of *radiation*. Radiation is particles or waves that carry energy. High-energy radiation can cause serious health problems. Although engineers could design spacecraft and spacesuits that could block out some forms of radiation, other forms of radiation cannot be easily blocked. Any person traveling to Mars will have to face some radiation.

It may be many years before people travel to Mars. The voyages of Curiosity and other robotic spacecraft may lead the way. They will continue analyzing Mars's crust and atmosphere and exploring different areas of the planet's surface. Who knows? Perhaps one of the robot rovers will find a relatively safe place for people to visit. ◆

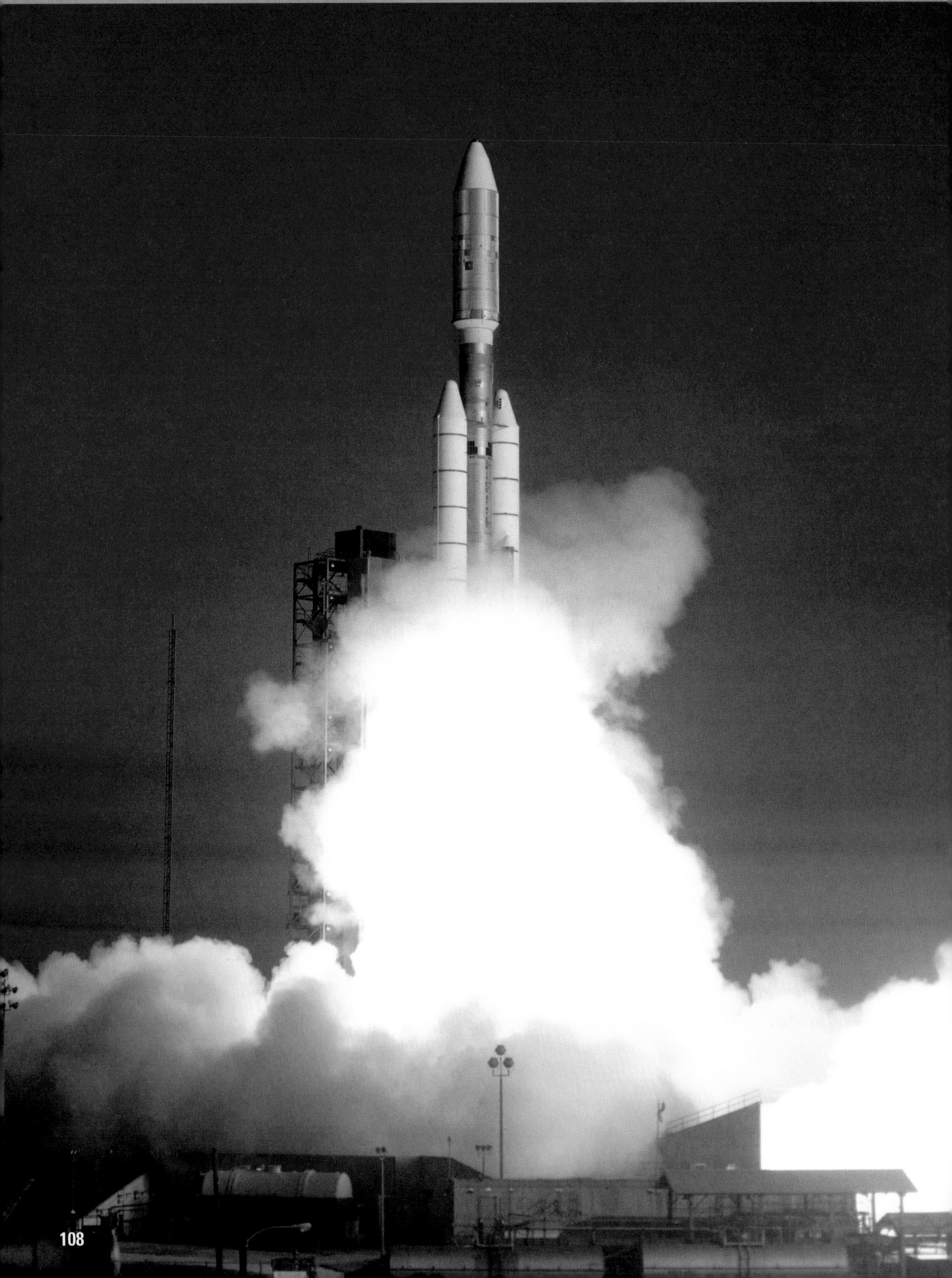

The Outer Solar System

What are the characteristics of the gas planets?

Introduction

"5, 4, 3, 2, 1… We have a liftoff!" On September 5, 1977, the Voyager 1 spacecraft was launched from Cape Canaveral, Florida. It was the last of four NASA spacecraft launched in the 1970s that were sent to explore the outer solar system. The outer solar system is the part of the solar system that includes Jupiter, Saturn, Uranus, and Neptune. Voyager 1 flew by Jupiter and Saturn before drifting off past Uranus's and Neptune's orbits. What information did Voyager 1 learn about these planets?

Voyager 1 flew by planets in the outer solar system. Previously, you used models to learn about the inner solar system. Now you will explore the outer solar system using similar models. These models, along with images and diagrams, will help you conceptualize the vast scale of the outer solar system.

After learning about the challenges of exploring the outer solar system, you will learn about the characteristics of the different planets. You will compare their different characteristics to determine patterns. These patterns can be used to group different planets together. Finally, you will learn about the other celestial objects in the outer solar system, including the Kuiper Belt, the Oort Cloud, and the comets that travel to the inner solar system and back.

Vocabulary

gas planet a planet that has a deep atmosphere and no rocky surface

density a physical property of matter that describes the amount of mass in a unit of volume

scale the level of measurement being used

Next Generation Science Standards

Performance Expectations

MS-ESS1-3. Analyze and interpret data to determine scale properties of objects in the solar system.

MS-ETS1-3. Analyze data from tests to determine similarities and differences among several design solutions to identify the best characteristics of each that can be combined into a new solution to better meet the criteria for success.

Science and Engineering Practices

Analyzing and Interpreting Data Analyze and interpret data to determine similarities and differences in findings.

Crosscutting Concepts

Scale, Proportion, and Quantity Time, space, and energy phenomena can be observed at various scales using models to study systems that are too large or too small.

Interdependence of Science, Engineering, and Technology

Disciplinary Core Ideas

ESS1.B. The solar system consists of the sun and a collection of objects, including planets, their moons, and asteroids that are held in orbit around the sun by its gravitational pull on them.

ETS1.B. • There are systematic processes for evaluating solutions with respect to how well they meet the criteria and constraints of a problem.
• Sometimes parts of different solutions can be combined to create a solution that is better than any of its predecessors.

ETS1.C. Although one design may not perform the best across all tests, identifying the characteristics of the design that performed the best in each test can provide useful information for the redesign process—that is, some of those characteristics may be incorporated into the new design.

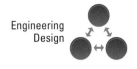

1. Engineering Spacecraft for the Outer Solar System

Suppose that you and your family are going on a surprise vacation. Without knowing what your destination is like, how would you prepare for your trip? Scientists and engineers designing the first spacecraft to explore the outer solar system had a similar problem. They did not know what conditions would be like once they got there. How could sending multiple spacecraft provide the data the teams needed to design successful missions?

Defining Criteria In the late 1960s, two teams of NASA scientists and engineers began working on spacecraft to travel to the outer solar system. The main criteria for these missions sound simple, but they were difficult engineering challenges. The spacecraft had to carry tools to collect data and send the data back to Earth. Since nobody would be traveling on them, the spacecraft and the tools had to be controlled by people on Earth. And one more thing: the spacecraft had to survive the trip through the outer planets.

Scientists knew that the radiation around Jupiter could harm the spacecraft on their journeys. Jupiter's radiation is made of high-energy charged particles, which can damage electronic tools. Scientists did not know how strong the radiation would be.

Pioneer 10, shown here, and Pioneer 11 were the first spacecraft to travel to the outer solar system. One of their main jobs was to measure the radiation around Jupiter, which scientists worried might harm the Pioneer spacecraft and future spacecraft.

Designing the Pioneer Spacecraft

The team of scientists and engineers who launched their spacecraft first named their probes Pioneer 10 and Pioneer 11. Pioneer 10 launched in 1972, and Pioneer 11 launched in 1973.

The Pioneers carried tools to measure Jupiter's radiation. Data collected showed that Jupiter's radiation was much stronger than engineers had built the systems to resist. Pioneer 10 started to have problems when it got close to Jupiter. At the time, Pioneer 10 was so far away that any signal it sent took more than 45 minutes to reach Earth. Any signal sent from Earth took the same amount of time to get there. That meant that scientists and engineers could not fix problems as they saw them. Instead, they regularly sent signals to reset the spacecraft's systems in hopes that the systems would keep working. The spacecraft survived in working condition. It sent a lot of important data back to Earth including information about how strong Jupiter's radiation was.

Modifying the Design of the Voyager Spacecraft While
Pioneer 10 and Pioneer 11 were in space, a second team of scientists
and engineers was working on two new spacecraft. These two spacecraft would also travel to the outer solar system. They were named
Voyager 1 and Voyager 2.

Both Voyager spacecraft benefitted from lessons learned during the
Pioneer missions. Engineers analyzed data from the Pioneer missions
and modified the Voyagers' designs to better protect them from Jupiter's
radiation. They modified many parts to withstand the strong radiation
and also added new parts to shield the spacecraft from radiation.

The Pioneer 11 mission showed that a path past Saturn's orbit
was possible. So, the Voyager team knew that one of their spacecraft
might be able to travel to Uranus and Neptune. Engineers modified
the spacecraft's design so Voyager 1 and 2 would work while going to
the two farthest planets. They added devices to boost signals going to
and from Earth. They also linked many systems, so they could work
together to make changes in flight.

The Success of the Voyager Design Voyager 1 was launched
on September 5, 1977. It was actually the second of the two spacecraft
to be launched. But Voyager 1 took a faster
path to Jupiter. So, it reached the planet
first. It reached Jupiter in 1979 and Saturn
in 1980. It collected data about both planets
and their moons.

When Voyager 2 was launched on
August 20, 1977, its main missions were
to visit Jupiter and Saturn. Figure 7.1
shows that after Voyager 2 completed its
Saturn flyby, scientists sent it to Uranus
and Neptune. So far, Voyager 2 is the only
spacecraft to have visited the last two planets
in the solar system.

Both Voyagers have traveled distances
many times the radius of Neptune's orbit.
They are still traveling away from the sun,
collecting data about space and sending them
back to Earth. The fact that the Voyagers
continue to work shows how well designed
they were. The added radiation shielding has
probably protected the spacecraft over the
years. The linked systems have changed how
the spacecraft collect data. These changes
made the Voyagers more useful than
scientists and engineers had ever planned.

Figure 7.1

The first four spacecraft sent to
the outer solar system each took
a different path. Scientists and
engineers modified the design of the
spacecraft to allow each one to travel
further and gather more data. All four
visited Jupiter, three visited Saturn,
and one visited Uranus and Neptune.

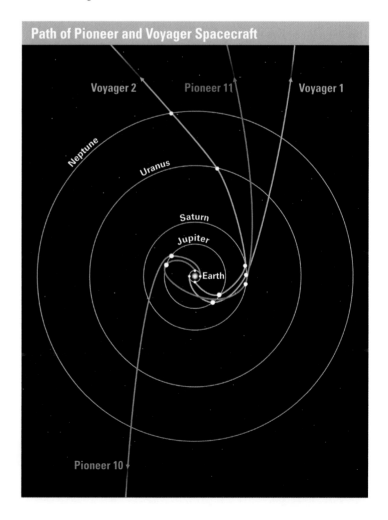

Path of Pioneer and Voyager Spacecraft

Voyager 2   Pioneer 11   Voyager 1

Neptune

Uranus

Saturn

Jupiter

Earth

Pioneer 10

2. Key Characteristics of the Gas Planets

Many people are developing ways to live on Mars, yet there are four more planets in the outer system. Why are people not looking at settling on those planets?

Jupiter, Saturn, Uranus, and Neptune make up the outer solar system. Each of these planets is a gas planet. A **gas planet** is a planet that has a deep atmosphere and no rocky surface. The lack of a rocky surface means that scientists can never land a spacecraft on any gas planet. The pressure at the surface would be so high that no spacecraft would survive!

Gravitational Forces and Density The outer solar system planets have huge masses compared to the inner solar system planets. Jupiter is the most massive planet, with a mass almost 318 times greater than Earth's mass. Even Uranus, the gas planet that has the smallest mass, is more than 14 times as massive as Earth is.

The large masses of the gas planets mean that they exert strong gravitational forces on surrounding objects. These large gravitational forces hold very light gases together to form the planet. The light gases that make up a lot of the gas planets are hydrogen and helium.

Figure 7.2A shows that the gas planets also have huge volumes compared to the terrestrial planets. Neptune is the gas planet with the smallest volume, and it takes up as much space as more than 57 Earths!

The gas planets' large masses and volumes are on a completely different scale than the terrestrial planets. A scale is the level of measurement that is being used. The outer planets are so large that people often use two different scales to compare the size of the outer and the inner planets.

Figure 7.2A

This diagram shows the volumes of the planets to scale. The four gas planets are huge compared to the four terrestrial planets. The gas planets have both a greater volume and have greater masses.

Scale Model of Planet Volumes

Terrestrial Planets — Mercury — Venus — Earth — Mars

Gaseous Planets — Jupiter — Saturn — Uranus — Neptune

You may have noticed that both Uranus and Neptune were described as being the "smallest" gas planet. How can both be the smallest? The answer has to do with the planets' densities. **Density** is mass per unit of volume. Uranus has a lower average density than Neptune. Uranus takes up more space than Neptune, but it has less mass, so its mass is more spread out than Neptune's mass.

However, both Uranus and Neptune are much less dense than terrestrial planets. Figure 7.2B shows that gases are less dense than rocks. Therefore, gas planets have lower average densities than terrestrial planets since a lot of gas planets' volumes are made up of light gases.

Orbital Characteristics Like the terrestrial planets, all of the gas planets revolve around the sun in a counterclockwise direction. However, a year on a gas planet is much longer than a year on a terrestrial planet. This is because the orbital radii of the outer planets is much greater than those of the inner planets. Outer planets have long years because their orbits are very large ellipses. The farther a planet is from the sun, the larger an ellipse it traces. So, the gas planets travel farther in a single revolution than the terrestrial planets do.

The gas planets rotate faster than the terrestrial planets do. So, a day on each gas planet is shorter than a day on any of the terrestrial planets.

Moons and Rings The large masses of the gas planets mean that the gravitational forces around the planets are strong enough to hold many moons in orbit around each planet at large orbital distances. For instance, Jupiter has more than 60 confirmed moons! These large planets are each in the center of a system of moons. The large gravitational forces also hold rings around each planet. The rings are made of dust, rock, and ice.

Like terrestrial planets, gas planets revolve around the sun and rotate on their axes. But gas planets are different in that they have large masses, which give them strong gravitational forces. Gas planets also have large volumes, which make the densities of the planets low despite their large masses. Because of their low densities, it is unlikely that humans will ever settle on a gas planet.

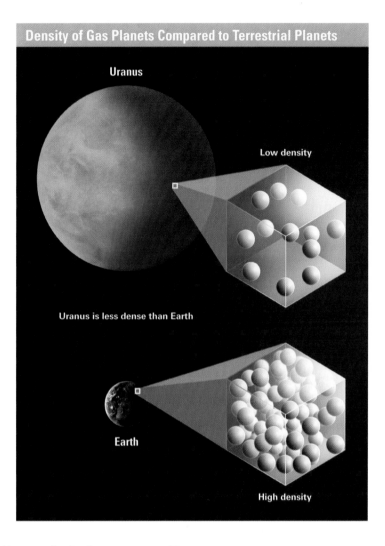

Density of Gas Planets Compared to Terrestrial Planets

Uranus

Low density

Uranus is less dense than Earth

Earth

High density

Figure 7.2B

Gas planets are less dense on average than terrestrial planets because a lot of their large volumes are made up of light gases. Much of the volume of a terrestrial planet is made of dense rock or metal. Because of their higher densities, terrestrial planets on average have more particles of matter in the same unit of volume.

Jupiter is the most massive planet in the solar system, and its moon Io is a little larger than Earth's moon. In this photo, Io casts a shadow on Jupiter causing a solar eclipse on the planet.

3. Jupiter

Jupiter is the solar system's most massive planet. It is so massive that engineers used Jupiter's mass and gravity to slingshot Voyager 2 out toward the other gas planets. Jupiter has such a huge volume that more than 1,000 Earths could fit inside the planet.

Jupiter's Gravitational Force and Density Amazingly, Jupiter's mass is more than twice the mass of all the other planets combined. Because Jupiter is so massive, it also has a strong gravitational field around it. This strong force holds particles of less massive substances together to form the planet. In fact, Jupiter is made mostly of hydrogen and helium, the two lightest gases.

Jupiter is the solar system's largest planet in volume, as well as mass. Jupiter's composition of light substances and its large volume combine to give Jupiter a relatively low density. Its average density is about one-fourth that of Earth.

Jupiter's Orbital Characteristics Jupiter rotates the fastest of all the planets in the solar system. One day on Jupiter is just under 10 hours long. Imagine trying to sleep, eat, and go to school in that amount of time. Your school days would have to be much shorter. However, the school year would be much longer. Jupiter has an orbital radius of 5.2 AU from the sun, which is 5.2 times further away than Earth is from the sun. As a result, a year on Jupiter is almost 12 Earth years long.

Jupiter's Moons and Rings

The Italian astronomer Galileo Galilei discovered Jupiter's four largest rocky moons in 1610 when he pointed his newly-improved telescope at the planet. They were the first group of moons found revolving around a planet.

The moons that Galileo discovered are named Io, Europa, Ganymede, and Callisto. Io has the most volcanic activity of any object in the solar system. Europa is covered in ice and may have a cold ocean of water under the ice. Some scientists think that Europa might have more water than Earth does, and may even have life under the ice. Ganymede and Callisto are the largest and the third largest moons in the solar system. In fact, Ganymede is larger than Mercury! These moons are denser than Jupiter because they are rocky like the terrestrial planets.

Jupiter has more than 60 known moons. Galileo discovered Jupiter's four largest moons. Then, the Voyager missions discovered a few of Jupiter's moons. But scientists discovered most of the moons using powerful ground-based telescopes.

Jupiter's rings were discovered in 1979 as technology to observe space improved. The rings had not been visible from Earth, and neither Pioneer 10 nor Pioneer 11 saw them when they flew by. So, when Voyager 1 flew by Jupiter and took the first photos of the planet's faint rings, people were surprised. Since their discovery, scientists have learned that the rings are made of dust that has come off some of Jupiter's many moons.

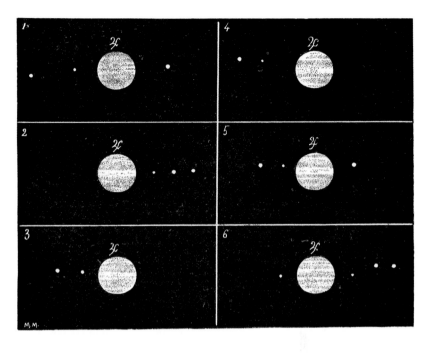

Galileo drew this sketch after viewing Jupiter and its four largest moons through his telescope.

Jupiter's four largest moons are shown to scale in this image. Ganymede is larger than Mercury and Io is larger than Earth's moon. These rocky moons are denser than Jupiter because they are not primarily composed of gas.

4. Saturn

When you think of the planet Saturn, the first thing you probably think of is its rings. But there was a time when people did not know the rings existed. It was not until Dutch astronomer Christiaan Huygens improved the methods he used to grind and polish his lenses in 1659 that Saturn's rings were identified.

Saturn's Gravitational Force and Density Saturn is the second largest planet in our solar system in both mass and volume. Its mass is 95 times greater than Earth's mass. Yet, Saturn's mass is still less than one third of Jupiter's mass.

Saturn exerts strong forces on nearby objects because it has such a large mass. Like Jupiter, Saturn is made mostly of hydrogen and helium. The strong gravitational forces hold these light gases together.

However, Saturn has less mass than Jupiter, so the forces it exerts are weaker. The particles of hydrogen and helium that make up Saturn are not packed together as tightly as they are on Jupiter. As a result, Saturn's density is lower than Jupiter's density. In fact, Saturn has the lowest density of all the planets in the solar system.

Saturn's Orbital Characteristics Saturn rotates at almost the same speed as Jupiter. One day on Saturn is on average ten and a half hours long. Saturn rotates around an axis that is tilted like Earth's axis. Saturn has an orbital radius of 9.5 AU from the sun; the long orbit results in a long year. It takes more than 29 Earth years for Saturn to go around the sun once.

Saturn is the solar system's second most massive planet and has the largest ring system of all the gas planets. Strong gravitational forces hold light gases together to form the planet. Saturn's large orbital radius results in a long year.

Saturn's rings appear only as a thin line in this photo because they are viewed from their edge, but the rings' shadow on Saturn's surface show they are much wider. Saturn's moon Titan looks smooth because it is covered with thick clouds.

Saturn's Moons and Rings In addition to identifying Saturn's rings, Huygens also discovered Saturn's largest moon Titan. Saturn has 62 or more moons. Scientists using powerful ground-based telescopes discovered most of Saturn's moons. Scientists using tools on a spacecraft named Cassini also discovered a few moons. However, Titan is not just Saturn's largest moon; it is also the second largest moon in the solar system. It is larger than the planet Mercury! Titan has liquid on its surface, but the liquid on Titan is not water. It is mostly a substance called methane. On Earth, methane is usually a gas, not a liquid.

In 2005, a spacecraft named Huygens (named after Christiaan Huygens) touched down on Titan's rocky surface. It was the first spacecraft to land in the outer solar system. Scientists used tools on the Huygens spacecraft to study Titan's atmosphere and take photos of the moon's surface. They found that Titan was covered in rock and sand-like pieces of organic material. The mission also found that there may be an ocean of liquid water under Titan's icy surface.

Saturn's rings were the first planetary rings to be discovered because they are easily seen from Earth with a telescope. The rings are easy to see because they are wide and made of ice and rock. The ice and rock reflect a lot of sunlight, which makes the rings shine brightly. The rings are more than 280,000 km wide, which is about three-fourths of the distance between Earth and the moon. In comparison, the rings are very thin. The main rings are only 10 meters thick! If you put the bottom of Saturn's rings on Earth, they would be only as tall as a three-story building. However, these same rings would stretch out into space past Earth's atmosphere.

5. Uranus

Uranus was the first planet to be discovered using a telescope. In 1781, British astronomer William Herschel noticed that Uranus appeared to be a fuzzy disk when observed through a telescope. Previously, people thought Uranus was a dim star. However, stars are so far away that they look like pinpoints of light, not disks. Herschel decided that the disk must be a planet that was farther away from the sun than Saturn was.

Uranus's Gravitational Force and Density Uranus has the smallest mass of all the gas planets, which means that Uranus's gravitational force on its atmosphere is weaker than the other gas planets. However, this gravitational force is still strong enough to hold a thick atmosphere made mostly of hydrogen and helium.

Uranus has the second smallest volume of the gas planets. But it is still much larger than Earth. Uranus's density is about the same as Jupiter's density.

Uranus's Orbital Characteristics One of the strangest things about Uranus is its rotation. Uranus's axis is almost parallel with its orbital plane, so it appears to rotate on its side. It also rotates in the direction opposite from most of the planets. Like Venus, Uranus rotates east to west. Unlike Venus, Uranus rotates more quickly than Earth. A day on Uranus is a little more than 17 Earth hours long. Scientists are still studying why Uranus's rotation is so different.

Uranus is about twice as far from the sun as Saturn is. It has an orbital radius of 19.2 AU. This long orbit means that Uranus revolves slowly around the sun. A year on Uranus is 84 Earth years long.

Uranus is the seventh planet from the sun in our solar system. These two photos show the front and the back of Uranus. Its rings are almost perpendicular to Uranus's orbital plane because the planet's axis is almost parallel to the orbital plane.

Uranus's Rings and Moons In 1977, two separate scientific teams discovered Uranus's rings using a telescope on an airplane. At the time, the teams found six rings. Since then, astronomers using Voyager 2 and the Hubble Space Telescope have found seven more rings around Uranus.

Uranus has at least 27 moons. William Herschel discovered the first two moons in 1787. When Voyager 2 visited Uranus in 1986, only five moons had been found. Scientists studying images taken by Voyager 2 found 11 more moons. Scientists using the Hubble Space Telescope and large ground-based telescopes discovered the moons.

6. Neptune

The first seven planets in the solar system were discovered by visual observations. But Neptune was discovered using mathematics. Scientists noticed that Uranus was not moving in its orbit the way they expected it to. A French mathematician named Urbain Joseph Le Verrier thought that a gravitational force from a yet undiscovered planet was pulling Uranus. Le Verrier used math to calculate where the new planet should be. He gave his notes to astronomers named Johann Gottfried Galle and Heinrich Louis d'Arrest, who, in 1846, found Neptune right where Le Verrier predicted.

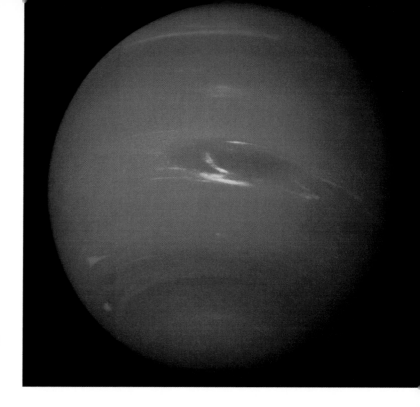

Neptune's Gravitational Force and Density Neptune has a greater mass than Uranus but less mass than Jupiter and Saturn. The gravitational forces between Neptune and light substances hold many of these light substances in Neptune's atmosphere. These substances include hydrogen and helium.

Neptune has the smallest volume of the gas planets. But it also has the highest density of those four planets. Thus, the particles of matter that make up Neptune are on average more tightly packed than the particles of matter that make up Jupiter, Saturn, and Uranus.

Neptune's great mass means its atmosphere contains many light substances such as hydrogen and helium. Voyager 2 took this close-up photo of Neptune in 1989. The white bands are clouds that form streaks because of the planet's fast rotation.

Neptune's Orbital Properties Like all of the gas planets, Neptune rotates quickly. A day on Neptune is only about 16 hours long. The fast rotation causes Neptune's clouds to form streaks across the planet's surface.

Neptune is very far from the sun, so it has a huge orbit. The planet's orbital radius is about 30 AU. One year on Neptune is almost 165 Earth years long! Since its discovery in 1846, Neptune has revolved around the sun only once.

Neptune's Rings and Moons Neptune's rings were discovered in the 1980s. However, the rings are hard to see and at least one of them looks odd compared to other planetary rings. Scientists think the odd appearance may be caused by a moon that revolves just inside of the rings. That moon is named Galatea.

Neptune has at least 13 moons. Scientists discovered the first two moons by telescope and discovered the next six (including Galatea) by studying data collected by Voyager 2. Scientists using large ground-based telescopes discovered the rest of Neptune's moons.

Model of the Outer Solar System

The outer solar system is composed of the four gas planets, Jupiter, Saturn, Uranus, and Neptune; the Kuiper Belt and the dwarf planets in it; and comets. Gas planets can be characterized by their size, their orbital characteristics, and their moon and ring systems. In this model of the outer solar system, two different scales are used to show the relative volumes of the planets and their different orbital radii.

Neptune
Neptune is the farthest planet from the sun. It was discovered when a mathematician calculated its position from data about Uranus's orbit. Neptune has several rings including one unusual clumpy ring. The planet also has several moons.

Neptune

Kuiper Belt
The Kuiper Belt is a doughnut-shaped region that extends from about 30 AU to 55 AU from the sun. It contains the dwarf planets Pluto and Eris, as well as many comets and other objects that revolve around the sun.

Jupiter

Jupiter is the largest planet in the solar system. Its mass is greater than the mass of all other planets combined. Jupiter is known for its bright red and white stripes and its Great Red Spot. Strong gravitational forces hold more than 50 moons in orbit around the planet. Jupiter also has faint rings that were first seen by Voyager 1.

Saturn

Saturn is the second largest planet in the solar system and is known for its bright ring system. Saturn is very windy and has a very low density. Saturn's moon Titan is one of the other large objects in the solar system known to have liquid on its surface.

Uranus

Uranus was the first planet to be discovered using a telescope. Its axis is so tilted it appears to rotate on its side. It also rotates in the direction opposite to most other planets. Like the other gas planets, Uranus has rings and a large moon system.

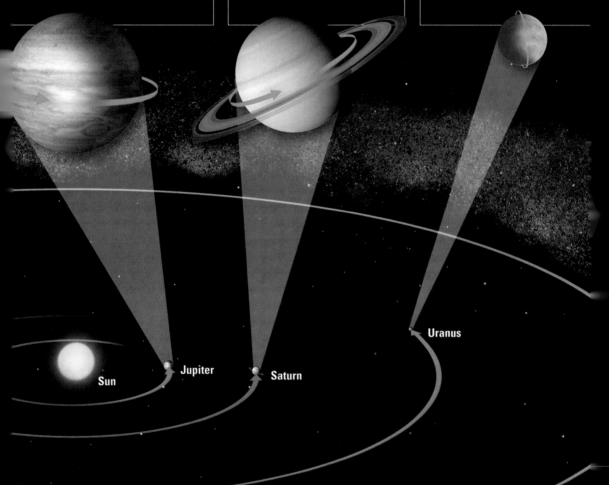

Planet	Crust Thickness	Atmosphere Height	Orbital Radius	Mass	Axial Tilt
Jupiter	None	200 km	5.2 AU	1898×10^{24} kg	3.1°
Saturn	None	700 km	9 AU	568×10^{24} kg	26.7°
Uranus	None	326 km	20 AU	87×10^{24} kg	97.8°
Neptune	None	225–239 km	30.1 AU	102×10^{24} kg	28.3°

7. Beyond Neptune

In June 2012, news sources declared that Voyager 1 had left the solar system. Then, every few months for more than a year, the same announcement was made. Finally, in September 2013, NASA said Voyager 1 had actually left the solar system. Why was it so hard to say when the spacecraft left? Scientists debate where the solar system ends. Voyager 1 has passed through the Kuiper Belt but has not reached the Oort Cloud, two regions at the edge of the solar system.

The Kuiper Belt The Kuiper Belt is a doughnut-shaped region of the solar system outside of Neptune's orbit that extends from about 30 AU to 55 AU from the sun. Scientists think it contains trillions of objects, including icy masses and comets.

The most famous Kuiper Belt object is the dwarf planet Pluto. Several other dwarf planets have been found in the Kuiper Belt, such as Eris and Makemake, and scientists think that many more have yet to be discovered. In 2015, the spacecraft New Horizons reached the Kuiper Belt with the mission to study the Kuiper Belt and visit Pluto.

The Oort Cloud Scientists believe the Oort Cloud is a ball-shaped part of the outer solar system that is 5,000 AU to 100,000 AU away from the sun. Like the Kuiper Belt, the Oort Cloud is filled with small, icy objects that become comets when disturbed.

Hundreds of billions, even trillions, of icy bodies may be in the Oort Cloud. If those objects exist, most cannot be seen from Earth. However, in 2003, scientists discovered an object that could be the first Oort Cloud object. The object is unofficially called Sedna, and it may be a dwarf planet.

Most comets come from the Kuiper Belt and the Oort Cloud. The Kuiper Belt is a doughnut-shaped area just outside of Neptune's orbit, and the Oort Cloud is a spherical-shaped volume far away from the sun.

Kuiper Belt

Oort Cloud

8. Comets

When comets are in the Kuiper Belt and the Oort Cloud, they seem to be boring, lumpy balls of ice. But when a comet's orbit brings it close to the sun, the comet becomes one of the most spectacular objects in the night sky.

Comets are made of ice and dust, and are built like giant, dirty snowballs. A comet's orbit, like all orbits, is an ellipse. But if a comet's orbit brings it close to the Sun, the ellipse is long and thin with the sun very close to one end. In that case, a comet spends most of its time far away from the sun. When the comet moves to the part of its orbit close to the sun, the sun heats the comet. The comet starts to give off gas and dust, which form two tails: a dust tail and an ion tail.

The dust tail of a comet is the brighter of the two tails and is usually the tail that people see most prominently from Earth. The ion tail is fainter than the dust trail and is made of electrically charged particles called *ions*. Generally, both tails point away from the sun.

This picture of comet Hale-Bopp was taken in 1997. The comet shows both the blue ion and the white dust tails, which trail off in the opposite direction from the sun.

LESSON SUMMARY

The Outer Solar System

Engineering Spacecraft for the Outer Solar System Engineers designing the Voyager spacecraft modified their design based on data collected by the Pioneer spacecraft.

Key Characteristics of the Gas Planets Gas planets have large masses, large volumes, many moons, and ring systems.

Jupiter Jupiter is the largest planet in the solar system, and its four largest moons were the first objects found to revolve around a planet other than Earth.

Saturn Saturn has the lowest density of all the planets and has the most elaborate ring system.

Uranus Uranus is the least massive gas planet, and it rotates on its side because its axis is very tilted.

Neptune Neptune has the smallest volume of the gas planets and is the farthest planet from the sun.

Beyond Neptune The Kuiper Belt and the Oort Cloud are two regions of the solar system that are far from the sun and are filled with icy objects.

Comets Comets usually originate from the Kuiper Belt or the Oort Cloud and sometimes have long, thin orbits that bring them close to the sun.

Comets: Signs of Doom?

In 2013, scientists around the world eagerly awaited the approach of Comet ISON toward the sun. If it survived its swing around the sun, it would be one of the brightest comets in decades. But a few people thought that ISON was an alien spacecraft on its way to attack Earth. Believing that a comet is a sign of doom is nothing new. Why have people found comets so mysterious and terrifying?

Ancient astronomers thought that comets were signs of impending doom; an idea reinforced when terrible events happened around the times that comets appeared. This timeline shows some historical events that coincided with comet sightings.

Astronomers, both ancient and modern, have kept careful track of celestial objects. They have had star charts that show where each visible star is located, and they have known that the planets move among the stars in relatively regular ways. So, when something unusual shows up in the sky, astronomers are surprised. Modern astronomers have some technology to determine and explain what the unusual object is, but ancient astronomers could not, which caused them to come up with explanations that may seem wild today.

Compared with other celestial objects, comets are very unusual. To the unaided eye, stars and planets look like points of light that keep about the same brightness. In contrast, from the first time a comet is noticed, it tends to increase in brightness and size. Once a comet is close enough to Earth, it looks like a fuzzy disk. When it gets even closer, it appears to have a tail. Throughout human history, people have observed comets that have had tails that would sometimes stretch more than halfway across the sky!

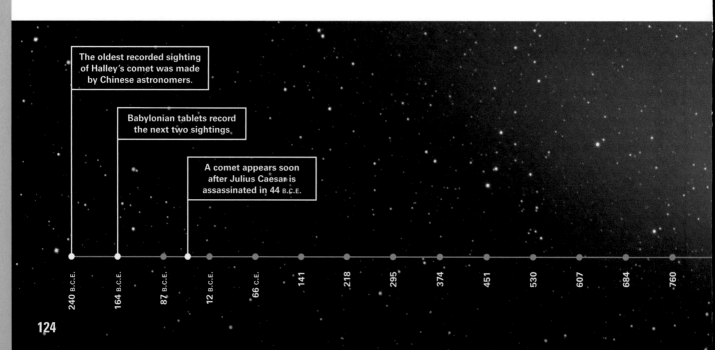

The oldest recorded sighting of Halley's comet was made by Chinese astronomers.

Babylonian tablets record the next two sightings.

A comet appears soon after Julius Caesar is assassinated in 44 B.C.E.

240 B.C.E.   164 B.C.E.   87 B.C.E.   12 B.C.E.   66 C.E.   141   218   295   374   451   530   607   684   760

For ancient astronomers, comets were terrifying indeed. They thought that the gods controlled the skies, and a comet was often taken to be a sign of trouble to come. This thought was supported when tragic events coincided with comet sightings.

Comet Coincidences

Several important events in history happened to occur around the same time that a comet was seen. For example, a very bright comet was seen shortly after Roman emperor Julius Caesar was killed in 44 B.C.E. The Romans thought that the comet was Caesar's soul haunting those responsible for his death.

In 1066, the comet that would be eventually known as Halley's Comet was seen just before William the Conqueror invaded England. People believed that the comet predicted the devastating invasion or, at least from William's point of view, glorious victory! The comet can even be seen in artwork called the Bayeux Tapestry, which tells the story of the invasion.

There was an outbreak in Europe of a deadly disease called the plague soon after the appearance of a comet in 1347. The plague, which was also called the Black Death, is estimated to have killed around 60 percent of the people in Europe. People thought that the comet brought the Black Death to Earth. In fact, it was called Comet Negra, which means "the black comet."

Another comet thought to have foretold death and destruction was seen by the Incas in South America. In 1532, soon after the comet was seen, the Spanish explorer Francisco Pizarro invaded the Incas' land and killed their emperor. While many people believed these comets were messages from the gods, others explained them as coincidences.

The Bayeux Tapestry depicts William the Conqueror invading England. This small section of the tapestry shows Halley's comet in at the top. People believed the invasion was foretold by Halley's comet.

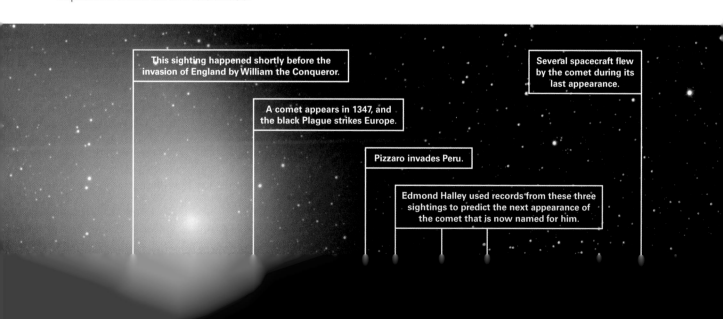

This sighting happened shortly before the invasion of England by William the Conqueror.

A comet appears in 1347, and the black Plague strikes Europe.

Several spacecraft flew by the comet during its last appearance.

Pizzaro invades Peru.

Edmond Halley used records from these three sightings to predict the next appearance of the comet that is now named for him.

Edmond Halley solved one of the big mysteries about comets. Halley determined that comets that fly by Earth, like this one observed in 2015, follow long, elliptical orbits in space.

Halley predicted that a comet seen in 1682 would reappear in 1758. His prediction was correct, and the comet, shown here, was named "Halley's Comet" after him.

Unlocking the Mysteries of Comets

By the early 1680s, astronomers knew that gravity held the planets in orbit around the sun, but comets were still mysterious. Comets were rarely seen and seemed to be unpredictable. Even the best astronomers had no idea how comets traveled through space.

The person who finally solved the mystery of a comet's path was the British scientist Edmond Halley. Halley was born in 1656 near London, England and went to college at Oxford University. In 1676, he left college without his degree to travel to the Southern Hemisphere, where he spent more than a year cataloging the stars in the Southern Hemisphere's sky. His catalog was so impressive that the king ordered Oxford University to give Halley a degree.

Over the next several years, Halley continued his work in math and a few different sciences. He was particularly good at organizing and making sense of large amounts of data. He created charts of ocean winds and designed mathematical tables that predicted the life expectancy of people in a population. Eventually, Halley turned his attention back to astronomy. This time, he was interested in cataloging comets.

Halley dug up records of comets seen in Europe from the 1470s to the 1690s, and he published the first catalog of comets in 1705. His careful study of the comets and their descriptions led him to conclude that the comets seen in 1531, 1607, and 1682 were the same comet. This comet came into view every 76 years. It appeared in regular intervals because it followed a long, skinny elliptical orbit. The orbit brought the comet close to Earth for a short time once during each trip around the sun. Other comets, Halley reasoned, also followed long elliptical orbits. However, each orbit was different, so the time between other comets' appearances would vary. Halley then predicted that the comet last seen in 1682 would return 76 years later in 1758.

Halley died in 1742 and never knew that his prediction was correct. The comet returned in 1758 and was named after him. Halley's Comet was last seen in 1986 and will not be seen again until 2061.

Comet Collisions

Although comets do not signal future disasters, a comet could cause serious problems if it were to strike Earth. Small asteroids and meteoroids enter Earth's atmosphere regularly, but until recently, scientists did not have direct observations of comets hitting any planet. That all changed in 1994 when the Shoemaker-Levy 9 Comet crashed into Jupiter. The comet had broken up into more than 20 pieces, and the pieces hit Jupiter with the force of millions of atomic bombs.

While the collisions of the comet were exciting to see, they also made people wonder, "What if the comet had hit Earth?" After observing Shoemaker-Levy 9's crash, scientists had a possible answer. If a comet the size of Shoemaker-Levy 9 would ever hit Earth, dust kicked up from the impact would block out sunlight, temperatures would drop, and many species might become extinct. In fact, some scientists think that the object that hit Earth and caused the extinction of the dinosaurs *was* a comet.

Scientists at NASA and all around the world are working to identify and keep track of all comets and asteroids that come near Earth. By keeping track of these objects, NASA hopes to be able to predict a possible comet or asteroid collision well before it happens.

Predicting doom makes for spine-tingling conversation and a good subject for blockbuster movies. But in reality, it is very, very unlikely that a comet will forecast doom. So, the next time a comet blazes in the sky, sit back and don't be afraid—just relax and enjoy its beauty. ◆

Impact sites

The photos show Jupiter before and after the Shoemaker-Levy 9 Comet hit Jupiter. One photo shows the pieces of the comet heading toward Jupiter, and the other photo shows the impact sites in Jupiter's atmosphere after the collisions of some of the comet pieces.

The Solar System and Beyond

OVERVIEW

It was billions of years ago that our solar system formed from a nebula, a cloud of dust and gas, like this one. Even now, solar systems are being born within nebulae throughout our Milky Way galaxy and other galaxies nearby. How do scientists explore the universe through time and space? What is the role of gravity throughout the universe? In this unit, you will find out gravity's role in the formation of the solar system and in the patterns you still see today. You will also model gravity's role beyond the solar system, in the Milky Way Galaxy and other galaxies around us.

Phenomenon-Based Storyline
You are a science consultant meeting with the director of a new space movie. Your role is to help ensure the movie is scientifically accurate as well as entertaining.

UNIT CONTENTS

Investigations Use models to correct misconceptions about how the solar system formed.

Investigations Use scale models to describe and compare distances between objects in the solar system and within the universe.

Engineering Challenge Develop multiple damping devices to protect a camera as it travels into space. Then test a design to identify points of failure and make improvements.

Performance Assessment
Using your knowledge, come up with and pitch a climax scene for a movie involving gravity. Utilizing a model, you will demonstrate how the scene is scientifically accurate while remaining entertaining.

UNIT 3

Connect Your Learning

The long passages of time and the vast distances in the universe are so great that it is hard to imagine them. What do they mean to you on Earth? How can patterns in our solar system and our galaxy, not to mention other galaxies, be connected to phenomena that you or scientists can observe right here on Earth?

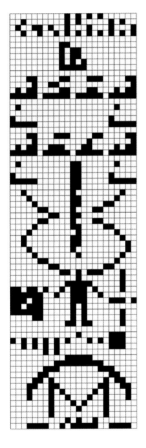

You will learn that the Milky Way galaxy is a vast pinwheel-shaped collection of stars. But from Earth, on a dark night, it looks like a band across the sky. Why does the Milky Way look different from Earth?

The Solar System and Beyond

Is there intelligent life in the universe beyond planet Earth? This image is from a digital message scientists have sent out to help answer that question. What does it communicate about your home planet?

Though our solar system formed billions of years ago, scientists are continuing to come to new insights on how it formed. How do scientists use clues found in meteoroids on Earth to piece together how the solar system formed?

Formation of the Solar System

....

How did the solar system form?

Introduction

If you go far from the city lights, you can see a night sky full of stars. Where did these stars come from? Stars may seem like they have been in the sky forever, but stars and the systems surrounding them are formed slowly. In fact, scientists believe that our solar system was formed in a nebula similar to the Orion Nebula shown here.

Since our solar system formed a long time ago, scientists cannot observe how it formed. So how can scientists come up with a theory? It is similar to explaining how a peanut butter and jelly sandwich was made. Almost all of these types of sandwiches have the same structure. There is a slice of bread, a layer of peanut butter, a layer of jelly, and another slice of bread. You put peanut butter on one slice of bread, jelly on the other slice, and then put the slices together.

Just as you can guess how a sandwich was made by looking at its structure, scientists looked at the patterns in the solar system to develop a theory on how our solar system was formed. One of the big ideas in science is that all natural systems and events follow consistent patterns. If a scientist observes the same pattern many times, then he or she can assume that these situations have similar, if not identical, causes. By studying pictures of nebulas and observing patterns, scientists can make predictions about how our solar system formed.

You will learn about the many patterns scientists have observed about the solar system. Then you will learn about the theory that scientists have come up with to explain these patterns. Just as you can figure out how a peanut butter and jelly sandwich was made, scientists can figure out how our solar system formed by observing patterns!

Vocabulary

scientific theory a well-tested explanation of scientific observations and experiments

nebula a large cloud of gas and dust in space

supernova a gigantic explosion of a large star

evidence information that supports or refutes a theory

Next Generation Science Standards

Performance Expectations
MS-ESS1-2. Develop and use a model to describe the role of gravity in the motions within galaxies and the solar system.

Science and Engineering Practices
Developing and Using Models Develop and use a model to describe phenomena.

Crosscutting Concepts
Patterns Patterns can be used to identify cause and effect relationships.
Systems and System Models Models can be used to represent systems and their interactions.
Scientific Knowledge Assumes an Order and Consistency in Natural Systems

Disciplinary Core Ideas
ESS1.B. The solar system appears to have formed from a disk of dust and gas, drawn together by gravity.

1. Recognizing Patterns in the Solar System

Scientists estimate that the solar system started to form about 4.6 billion years ago. That means the solar system took longer to form than humans have existed. How did scientists come up with this theory?

A **scientific theory** is a well-tested explanation of scientific observations and experiments. Though scientists cannot observe the formation of the solar system, they can observe patterns and find similar situations where the same patterns occur. They can then use these observations to come up with a theory about how solar systems are formed. What patterns did scientists observe?

Patterns in Orbit One pattern that scientists use to study the formation of the solar system is the revolution of the planets. All the planets revolve around the sun in the same direction. When viewed from above the North Pole, Earth, and the other planets revolve counterclockwise. The dwarf planets and most other objects in the solar system revolve in that direction, too. Most of the moons in the solar system revolve counterclockwise around their planets, as well.

The planets' orbits also have patterns. All the planets' orbits are ellipses that are nearly circular in shape. The sun is near the center of each orbit. As a result, the orbits of the planets do not cross, and the distance between any two orbits stays about the same. The orbits also all lie in nearly the same orbital plane.

A Pattern in Rotation Another pattern can be seen in the rotation of planets. Six of the eight planets rotate from west to east. Only Venus and Uranus do not. Venus rotates from east to west, and Uranus rotates on its side. Thus, the sun rises toward the east on all planets except Venus and Uranus. Many of the dwarf planets also rotate from west to east. So, most planets and dwarf planets rotate in the same direction that they revolve around the sun.

Patterns in Structure and Size Another pattern is the structure and size of planets. The inner solar system planets are all terrestrial planets, and the outer solar system planets are all gas planets. Inner solar system planets are also much smaller than outer solar system planets. Even the largest terrestrial planet, Earth, is tiny compared to Neptune, the smallest gas planet.

Figure 8.1

If you could see the solar system from far above Earth's North Pole, you could watch the planets rotate on their axes as they revolve around the sun. Most planets and dwarf planets revolve in a counterclockwise motion.

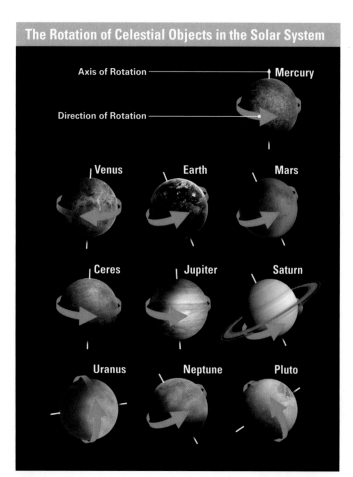

The Rotation of Celestial Objects in the Solar System

Axis of Rotation — Mercury

Direction of Rotation

Venus   Earth   Mars

Ceres   Jupiter   Saturn

Uranus   Neptune   Pluto

2. Gravity and the Beginning of Our Solar System

Though our solar system formed many years ago, scientists carefully observed all of these patterns. They developed a scientific theory that described how the solar system formed while also explaining the patterns they observed. What theory did scientists come up with?

The Nebular Theory explains how solar systems form. First, our solar system started to form from a nebula. A **nebula** is a large cloud of gas and dust in space. You can see part of a nebula in the photo. Many stars and planets form from the matter in one nebula. The solar system started to form when something caused some of the matter in a nebula to clump up. Scientists are not sure what that "something" was, but many scientists think that it was a nearby supernova. A **supernova** is a gigantic explosion of a very massive star. The force from the supernova may have pushed matter in the nebula together.

As the matter was pushed together, the gravitational forces between the particles pulled them even closer together. As they got closer and closer, the nebula began to collapse, and the matter in the nebula started to rotate around its center. Gravitational forces between particles pulled the matter closer together, and the nebula started to rotate faster. As it rotated faster, the nebula flattened into a disk. Meanwhile, the center of the nebula kept getting denser and hotter.

The matter in the center of the nebula would eventually form the sun. The remaining matter continued to rotate in the disk. Much of that matter would eventually form the planets. The sun and the planets still rotate in the same direction as the nebula did. This pattern supports the Nebular Theory.

Our solar system formed in a nebula similar to the Eagle Nebula, shown here. As gravitational forces between particles of matter pulled them together, stars began to form. New stars and solar systems may be forming in the Eagle Nebula right now.

The matter that eventually became the planets of the solar system rotated in a flat disk around the hot center of the nebula. Initially, the dust and gas particles ran into each other and stuck together because of gravitational and other forces between them.

3. The Formation and Growth of the Planets

Have you ever seen a snowball roll down a hill? You may have noticed that the snowball grows larger and larger as it rolls. Though snowflakes are tiny, they stick together and form big clumps as they run into each other. How is the way a snowball grows similar to how the planets started to form?

Gas and Dust Revolves in the Same Direction Recall that the matter in the nebula that eventually formed the solar system was in a disk that revolved around a hot center. As the bits of dust and gas particles revolved, they ran into each other and stuck together due to gravitational and other forces. Just as gravitational forces hold you to the surface of Earth, these forces between the tiny particles of gas and dust caused them to group together.

Slowly, the dust and gas particles formed distinct clumps. The clumps ran into each other and formed larger clumps. As the clumps grew larger, they started sweeping up matter faster.

Eventually, some clumps grew to the size of a few kilometers across. These clumps are called *planetesimals*, which means "small planets." Gravitational forces between the planetesimals and particles of dust and gas caused the planetesimals to grow bigger as they ran into more matter. This is similar to how snowballs grow bigger as they roll down a hill, picking up snow as they travel. Unlike snowballs, which lump together as they melt and freeze, the gas and dust particles were not melting or freezing. Gravitational and other forces between each particle were enough to hold them together. Some of the planetesimals would become the planets in the solar system.

The dust and gas in the rotating nebula formed a disk around its center. A disk, of course, is relatively flat. So, when the planets started to form, they formed in the same plane as the disk. Today, the planets still revolve around the sun in that plane, which is the orbital plane of the planets.

Planetesimals Rotate in the Same Direction As the clumps and planetesimals formed, they rotated too. Most likely they all rotated in the same counterclockwise direction as they revolved around the center of the nebula. Most of the planets still rotate in that direction. Scientists are not sure why Venus and Uranus rotate differently from the rest of the planets. They think that both planets started rotating in the normal direction but some unknown factor caused their rotations to change. One hypothesis is that large objects hit Venus and Uranus, which caused the planets to spin in another direction. So, Venus is still rotating in the same direction that it always has, but now it is rotating upside-down, or "on its head."

Terrestrial and Gas Planets Form The center of the rotating nebula was very hot. So, the part of the disk that was close to the center was warmer than the part of the disk that was farther away. As the clumps of dust formed, only particles of heavier substances came together near the center. Lighter substances were gases at this temperature. These heavy substances were particles of metals and compounds now found in rock. The planetesimals and planets that formed near the nebula's center were rocky and contained metal. As a result, the inner solar system contains terrestrial planets and rocky asteroids.

Further away from the center of the nebula, space was much cooler. There, compounds such as water, methane, and ammonia froze to form icy cores. As these planetesimals formed and grew bigger, gases such as hydrogen and helium were held close to the core by gravitational forces. Thus, the outer solar system contains gas planets and icy objects.

The theory on how the solar system formed explains many patterns. It explains why the planets revolve in the same direction as the sun rotates, why most planets rotate in the same direction, and why terrestrial planets are near the sun and gas planets are far away.

As matter in the nebula came together, it formed large chunks called planetesimals. Some of the planetesimals became the planets, and the compositions of the planets were determined mostly by the distance between the planetesimals and the hot center of the nebula.

Gravity and the Formation of the Solar System

The solar system was formed by a nebula about 4.6 billion years ago. Though people cannot go back in time to see how our solar system formed, astronomers observed patterns in our solar system and other solar systems to develop the Nebular Theory. All of these patterns that we observe now are related to how it formed billions of years ago. This diagram models the process for how our solar system formed.

4.6 Billion Years Ago

About 4.6 billion years ago, something, possibly a supernova, caused the dust and gas in the nebula to start to come together. Gravitational forces between the particles pulled them together, and the nebula started to rotate.

As the nebula collapsed, it formed a flat spinning disk of dust and gas. Over millions of years, the gas and dust would eventually form the planets as we know them now.

Over millions of years, the nebula rotated faster while most of the matter was pulled to the center by gravitational forces. The center was a hot dense area that would eventually become the sun. Dust and gas particles formed clumps on the same plane as the disk.

As they revolved in the same direction around the center, the dust and gas clumps grew larger due to their gravitational forces. Heavier substances clumped near the sun and formed the terrestrial planets. Lighter substances clumped further from the sun and formed the gas planets.

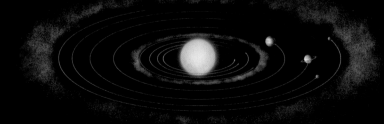

The Solar System Today

4. The Search for Other Solar Systems

Scientists cannot go back in time. But if their theory is correct, then other solar systems may be forming in the same way ours formed. Why do scientists believe that solar systems form in the same way?

Scientists assume that events, such as the formation of solar systems, follow consistent patterns. Astronomers look for solar systems that are in the process of forming and assume that the events they observe are similar to the events that led to the formation of *our* solar system.

To find these "baby" solar systems, scientists used data collected with orbiting space telescopes. One of those telescopes is called WISE. WISE took 2.7 million images of the universe. But finding baby solar systems in all those images will take time that scientists do not have. How are they going to find what they need? They are asking people to help. Scientists set up a website for people around the world to examine the images and find possible solar systems.

Even if a forming solar system is found, scientists cannot simply watch it to see what happens. A solar system takes millions of years to form. That is longer than humans have existed! Instead, scientists need to find many different solar systems at various stages of their formation to gather evidence. **Evidence** is information such as data, a model, or observations that support or refute a claim. Other solar systems are forming now similarly to how our own solar system formed long ago. Therefore, the data that they gather on other solar systems is valid evidence for describing how our solar system formed. As scientists gain more evidence, the theory on how solar systems formed may well improve and change, and become more accurate.

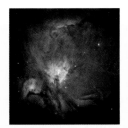

LESSON SUMMARY

Formation of the Solar System

Recognizing Patterns in the Solar System Scientists have identified several patterns in the solar system that are related to its formation.

Gravity and the Beginning of Our Solar System The solar system began to form when the force of an event, like a supernova explosion, pushed matter in a nebula together, which allowed gravitational forces to pull matter closer together.

The Formation and Growth of Planets Gravitational and other forces pulled dust and gas from the nebula together to form planets.

The Search for Other Solar Systems Scientists are looking for solar systems in the process of forming to gather evidence that supports or refutes their theory on how our solar system formed.

The Chilling Search for Solar System Secrets

WANTED: A research assistant for a scientific team studying the origin of the solar system. Must have a keen eye and a tolerance for cold weather. Ability to drive a snowmobile a plus.

How can driving a snowmobile help someone study the solar system? Snowmobile skills are important to scientists who hunt for meteorites in Antarctica. A meteorite is a naturally occurring piece of rock or metal that falls to Earth from space. Studying meteorites yields important clues about the solar system.

In December of every year, scientists leave the comforts of home to live in the coldest place on Earth for two months. December is the middle of the Antarctic "summer," and because of Earth's tilted axis, the sun stays above the horizon during the summer. Even with the sun up 24 hours a day, the temperature is usually well below 0°C, and water stays frozen!

Every year, scientists travel to the continent of Antarctica to search for meteorites. Although many visit during the summer, temperatures are still so cold that the scientists must dress in special clothing to stay warm.

Because of the extreme cold, life for the meteorite-hunting scientists in Antarctica is challenging. They live in small, specially-designed tents that are heated by tiny camp stoves. Even with the heat from the stoves, the scientists sleep fully-clothed in insulated sleeping bags. For some scientists, the only electricity they have is the small amount generated by solar panels on the tents. With no running water, there are no flush toilets, so the "facilities" consist of a bucket in a tent.

When the scientists go out to look for meteorites, they must dress for survival in layers of long underwear, fleece, thick coats, and insulated boots over thick socks. Heads are protected by hats, scarves, and ski masks designed to cover almost every bit of skin. Scientists' sunglasses cover even more skin and block out the bright, glaring sunlight reflected off the snow.

Lunar Meteorite | Martian Meteorite | Iron Meteorite

Where, Oh Where Did the Meteorite Land?

Why do scientists go so far from home to such an uncomfortable place to look for meteorites? The chances of finding meteorites are better in Antarctica than they are any place else on the planet. Dark-colored meteorites are easy to see on white snow, and rocks and soil do not cover up the meteorites after they fall. Meteorites are also more plentiful in Antarctica because those that fell and were buried thousands of years ago are slowly rising to the surface. With the lack of human habitation, they haven't been taken, rolled over by tractors, or plowed under fields and towns. Additionally, with the cold dry climate, the meteorites do not corrode easily.

Finding meteorites is possible if you can endure the cold. To hunt for meteorites, the researchers jump on their snowmobiles and drive slowly across the ice in a set pattern, scanning the ground for anything dark. If they see something dark, that something is probably a rock, and that rock may well be a meteorite.

The researchers line up their snowmobiles 30 meters apart and drive a straight line to avoid missing any meteorites. When they find one, they examine the rock and decide if the rock is an Earth rock or a space rock. To determine if a rock is a meteorite, the researchers look for certain features. Meteorites tend to be dark, shiny, and show characteristic marks from their heated trips through Earth's atmosphere.

In the field, meteorites look alike, but when they are cut open, their insides look different. What scientists see inside helps them figure out where the meteorites came from. The meteorites shown in the photos here likely came from the moon, Mars, and an asteroid!

Scientists search for meteorites in Antarctica because the rocks are easy to see on the ice and because the cold climate keeps them from corroding. All meteorites tend to be dark on the surface, but each is unique once it is cut open.

Cataloging, Collecting, and Classifying Meteorites

When the researchers agree that a rock is a meteorite, they have to catalog and collect it. The researchers record the meteorite's GPS location and write a description of it. They assign it a catalog number and photograph it on the ground. Only then do they pick up the meteorite with a tool that looks like a pair of tongs, drop it into a bag, and seal the bag. At no point in the whole collection process does anyone touch the meteorite. Touching it—even accidentally with a glove or a shoe—could contaminate it and alter its surface, which researchers want to study!

As much as the researchers would like to study the meteorites that they find, they cannot. At least, they cannot do so while in Antarctica. Instead, they carefully store the space rocks in freezer boxes to keep them frozen. At the end of the scientists' stay on the icy continent, they send the meteorites in their freezer boxes to different laboratories. Most American scientists send their meteorites to NASA's Johnson Space Center in Houston, Texas.

The meteorites are carefully thawed in a special lab. Scientists there thoroughly examine each meteorite and chip off small pieces to analyze. Again, this is all done without anyone touching the meteorite with bare hands. The Houston scientists classify the meteorites based on their composition, which can be mostly iron, mostly stone, or a mixture of iron and stone. After this initial examination, the meteorites are carefully stored.

About twice a year, the Houston scientists publish a newsletter that includes a list of all newly found meteorites, including the composition, the size, and a description of the appearance of each one. Any scientist around the world who wants to study meteorites can look through the list and apply to receive particular samples. The scientists who were part of the search team in Antarctica do not get special treatment when it comes to receiving samples. Although researchers spent almost two frozen months in tents and may have personally found a particular meteorite, they have to apply for the sample as any other scientist would. In other words, those scientists went to Antarctica solely for the reward of the experience and the chance to contribute to humanity's scientific knowledge of the universe!

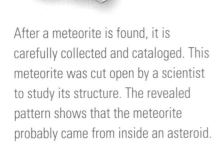

After a meteorite is found, it is carefully collected and cataloged. This meteorite was cut open by a scientist to study its structure. The revealed pattern shows that the meteorite probably came from inside an asteroid.

Revealing the Secrets of the Solar System

What can scientists learn about the meteorites that they receive? Scientists often start by trying to determine where the meteorite came from. Most meteorites come from the asteroid belt, and some meteorites come from the moon and Mars. Meteorites from other places in the solar system may exist. In fact, some scientists believe that they have found a meteorite that came from Mercury.

Many of the rocks in the asteroid belt formed early in the solar system's history. They are around 4.5 billion years old and are some of the oldest objects in the solar system. Scientists studying these meteorites can learn about what substances were in the early solar system. They can also learn how the meteorite formed, which gives clues about how larger objects such as moons and planets may have grown. Meteorites provide scientists with many clues about how the solar system was formed.

Scientists around the world are eager to unlock the secrets inside meteorites. Some are willing to endure the chilling experience of the meteorite hunt. After all, meteorite studies are a way of learning about the moon, asteroids, and planets without having to travel into space. Instead, scientists can go to Antarctica to find pieces of celestial objects conveniently delivered to Earth. ◆

Scientists can learn about how the solar system formed by studying meteorites. They use different techniques to study the meteorites, including looking at pieces of the rocks under microscopes. Some museums have meteorites and pieces of meteorites that you can examine and maybe even touch!

Beyond the Solar System

What are the scales of objects in the universe?

Introduction

Suppose you aim a telescope at a shining point in the night sky that you think may be a planet. When you look through it, instead of seeing a round planet, you see a bright swirl of light. You have just used a telescope to observe a galaxy! The galaxy in this image, called Messier 81 (or M81 for short), is one of the galaxies commonly sighted in the night sky by astronomers. What is a galaxy, and how does it relate to our solar system?

Previously, you learned about Earth, the moon, and the solar system. In this final lesson, you will learn that the solar system is part of the Milky Way galaxy. Think about Earth as your home. Then, the solar system is Earth's neighborhood. A neighborhood is a small part of a larger city, and a city is part of a larger state. Similarly, Earth's neighborhood, the solar system, is part of a larger "city," or a galaxy. Just as there are many cities in a state, the Milky Way is just one of billions of galaxies in the universe.

Using scale models, you will explore the vast distances in space. You will learn a unit of measurement used to describe the distances between stars. Scale models help show the distance between Earth and the center of the Milky Way. Additionally, they are used to help understand the distance between the Milky Way and other nearby galaxies, as well as the vastness of the universe. Engineers also use scale models to design telescopes that allow them to see deep into space.

Vocabulary

light-year a unit of length equal to the distance that light travels in space in one year

galaxy a collection of stars, dust, and gases held together by gravitational forces

black hole an object that is so dense that nothing within a certain distance from it can escape its gravitational field

universe all the space, time, matter, and energy that exists

Next Generation Science Standards

Performance Expectations
MS-ESS1-2. Develop and use a model to describe the role of gravity in the motions within galaxies and the solar system.

MS-ETS1-4. Develop a model to generate data for iterative testing and modification of a proposed object, tool, or process such that an optimal design can be achieved.

Science and Engineering Practices
Developing and Using Models • Develop and use a model to describe phenomena. • Develop a model to generate data to test ideas about

designed systems, including those representing inputs and outputs.

Crosscutting Concepts
Systems and System Models Models can be used to represent systems and their interactions.
Scale, Proportion, and Quantity Time, space, and energy phenomena can be observed at various scales using models to study systems that are too large or too small.
Scientific Knowledge Assumes an Order and Consistency in Natural Systems

Disciplinary Core Ideas
ESS1.A. Earth and its solar system are part of the Milky Way galaxy, which is one of many galaxies in the universe.

ETS1.B. • A solution needs to be tested, and then modified on the basis of the test results, in order to improve it. • Models of all kinds are important for testing solutions.

ETS1.C. The iterative process of testing the most promising solutions and modifying what is proposed on the basis of the test results leads to greater refinement and ultimately to an optimal solution.

1. Modeling Distances Between Stars

What unit would you use to measure the distance across the palm of your hand? What about the distance between two cities? You might use centimeters for your hand, but the centimeter is not as convenient if you want to measure the distance between cities. To do that, you would most likely want to use a larger unit, such as the kilometer. What units do scientists use when measuring distances between stars?

Units to Measure Distances in Space The moon is the closest celestial object to Earth. It is about 384,400 km away. For this distance, kilometers is a reasonable unit to use. All other objects in the solar system are much farther away. Scientists use astronomical units (AU) to measure most distances in the solar system. Recall that 1 AU is equal to the average distance between the sun and Earth. Astronomical units are useful because they are large enough to give distances in the solar system in small numbers. But astronomical units are not as useful when measuring the distances between stars.

The closest star to the sun is Proxima Centauri. It is about 271,000 AU away. Other stars are much farther away. Because the distances between stars are so huge, scientists use an even larger unit to describe those distances. A **light-year** (ly) is the distance that light travels in one year. One light-year is 9.46×10^{12} km, and the distance between stars range from a few light-years to billions of light-years. Proxima Centauri, the closest star to our sun, is 4.2 ly away. That is nearly 40 trillion kilometers away!

Figure 9.1

This scale model shows how the distances in the solar system compare with the distances between stars. This model shrinks 1 AU down to the length of an inch. At this scale, 1 ly is about the length of 1 mile. The distance between Earth and the sun is 1 inch, the width of Neptune's orbit is 60 inches (5 feet), and Proxima Centauri, the closest star to the sun, is 4.2 miles away.

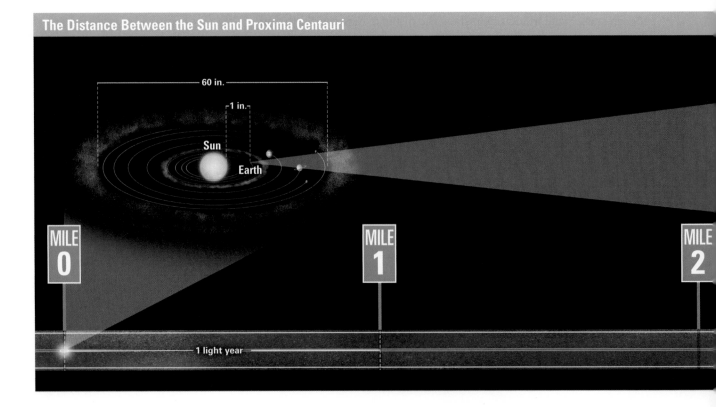

The Distance Between the Sun and Proxima Centauri

60 in.

1 in.

Sun

Earth

MILE 0

MILE 1

MILE 2

1 light year

A Model for Distances in Space The length of a light-year is difficult to imagine because it is so much longer than anything you have ever seen. So, a scale model that compares a light-year to units you are familiar with can be very helpful for understanding how far away other stars are from Earth.

In the scale model shown in Figure 9.1, 1 AU is equal to 1 inch. The number of inches in a mile is about the same as the number of astronomical units in a light-year. So, 1 ly is equal to about 1 mile in the scale model. Located at the very start of the roadway, the sun will be the size of a grain of sand less than 0.01 inch across. Earth will be a speck of dust, about 0.0001 inch in diameter, and located one inch away from the grain of sand representing the sun. The moon will be too small to see, but it will be the width of one human hair away from the speck of dust representing Earth.

The sun, the moon, and Earth are very close together in this roadway. Proxima Centauri, the closest star to the sun, will be a 4.2 mile ride away and will also be the size of a grain of sand. Other stars are even farther away. For example, the star at the end of the handle of the Big Dipper, Alkaid, is 104 ly away. This star would be 104 miles away on your model. It would take a long time riding your bike down this roadway to reach this star!

The distance between planets in the solar system seems very large. After all, Voyager 2 needed 12 years to travel from Earth to Neptune. But as you can see from the scale model, the distances in the solar system are tiny compared to the distances between stars.

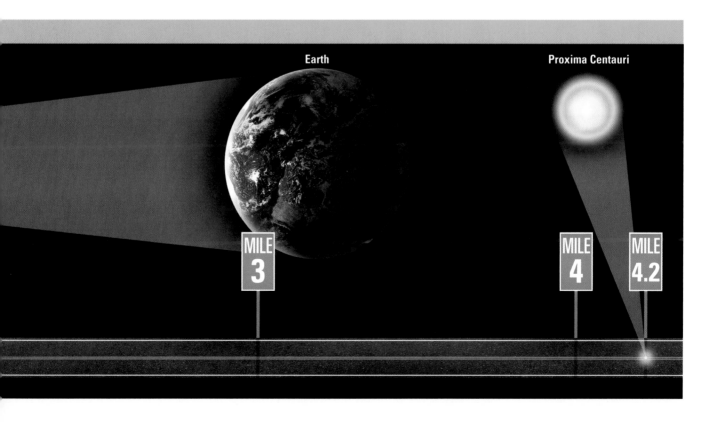

2. The Milky Way Galaxy

Suppose you are hiking at night in Zion National Park, Utah, or some other very dark place. The only human-made light source you can see is from your flashlight. When you turn off your flashlight and look up, you see a splotchy white glow stretching across the sky. That white strip is made up of far-away stars that are all, as our solar system is, part of the Milky Way galaxy. What is a galaxy?

Galaxies and Gravity Just as the sun's gravitational forces on other objects keep them in orbit around the sun, gravitational forces hold stars together in orbiting groups.

A **galaxy** is a collection of stars, dust, and gases held together by gravitational forces. The stars all attract each other, so they group together and revolve. In the center of most galaxies, there is usually a large, dense concentration of stars called a bulge. In the middle of that bulge, there is usually a black hole. A **black hole** is an object that is so dense that nothing, including light, within a certain distance from it can escape its gravity. Some black holes have about the same density as all of Earth's mass squeezed into an object the size of a golf ball.

The hazy white glow that stretches across the sky is called the Milky Way. The stars seen are, like the sun, part of the stellar disk of the Milky Way galaxy. Most of the stars in the galaxy form a narrow strip in the sky because the galaxy's disk is seen edge-on from Earth.

Because no light escapes a black hole, you might expect that the center of a galaxy is hard to see. However, when matter approaches a black hole, it heats up and glows. So, black holes near stars are often surrounded by a ring of hot, bright matter.

The Shape of the Milky Way By studying other galaxies, scientists have learned that most of the Milky Way is a disk of stars with a spiral shape. But if you look at the Milky Way in the sky, it looks like a narrow band of light. The Milky Way looks narrow from Earth because of the angle from which you are looking at it. If you look at a pizza from the side, it looks like a narrow rectangle. Similarly, people on Earth view the Milky Way edge-on, so it looks like a narrow strip of light, as seen in the photo.

However, if you look down from above at the top of the pizza, it will look like a circle. Likewise, if you were able to look down on the Milky Way from above, you would be able to see the galaxy's spiral shape as it rotates. You would also see that many stars are clumped around the central black hole. The clump of stars forms the galaxy's central bulge. The bulge is a huge sphere-shaped group of stars. About half of the sphere is above the galaxy's disk of stars and the other half is below the disk. The other stars in the Milky Way form a disk, with a pattern of spiral arms in the disk that swirls around the black hole. Our solar system is in one of the arms.

The Structure of the Milky Way Galaxy

Like all galaxies, the Milky Way is held together by gravitational forces. The supermassive black hole in the center of the galaxy exerts gravitational forces on the stars. As a result, the stars in the galaxy revolve around the black hole, similar to how the planets of our solar system rotate around the sun.

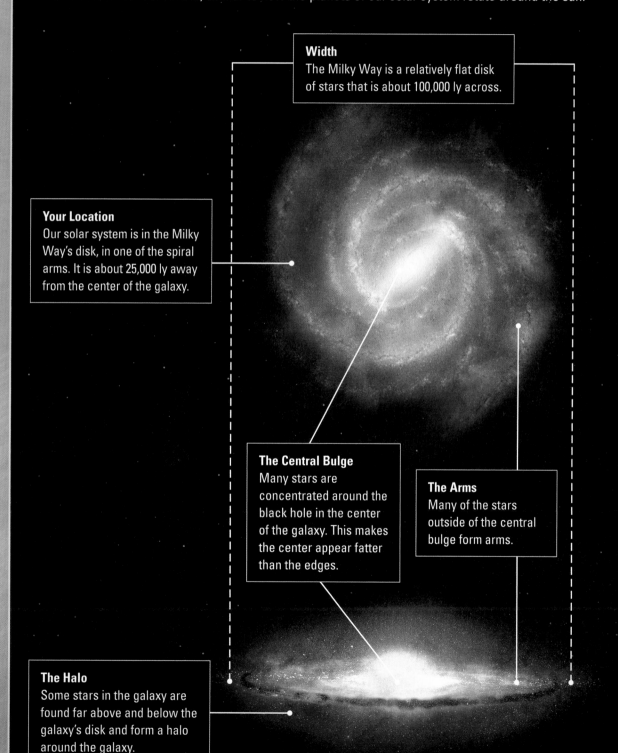

Width
The Milky Way is a relatively flat disk of stars that is about 100,000 ly across.

Your Location
Our solar system is in the Milky Way's disk, in one of the spiral arms. It is about 25,000 ly away from the center of the galaxy.

The Central Bulge
Many stars are concentrated around the black hole in the center of the galaxy. This makes the center appear fatter than the edges.

The Arms
Many of the stars outside of the central bulge form arms.

The Halo
Some stars in the galaxy are found far above and below the galaxy's disk and form a halo around the galaxy.

Spiral Galaxy

Elliptical Galaxy

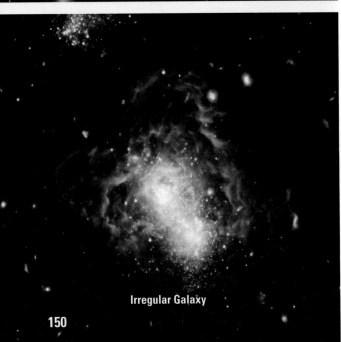

Irregular Galaxy

3. Types of Galaxies

The Milky Way was the only object known to be a galaxy until the 1920s. Then, the American astronomer Edwin Hubble proved that the great nebula in Andromeda was actually a galaxy outside of the Milky Way. By observing patterns in the brightness of stars, astronomers confirmed that many previously known "nebulae" were galaxies, too. They discovered many more galaxies and classified them by their appearance. Using powerful telescopes, astronomers can observe the appearance of galaxies and classify them into three groups. Today, many billions of galaxies are known to exist, and astronomers still use Edwin Hubble's classification system.

Spiral Galaxies The Andromeda galaxy and most of the known galaxies are spiral galaxies. Scientists determined that the Milky Way is a spiral galaxy by studying other spiral galaxies. They compared the motion of stars in other galaxies with the motion of stars in the Milky Way.

Elliptical Galaxies The second most common galaxy shape is the ellipsoid. These galaxies look like circles or ovals, but are actually spheres or flattened spheres; they do not have arms. Elliptical galaxies contain older stars than spiral galaxies do. They do not have as much gas and dust as spiral galaxies. Some of the largest galaxies known are elliptical galaxies.

Irregular Galaxies The galaxies in the last group are not spirals or ellipses. These galaxies are called irregular galaxies. Irregular galaxies tend to have many young stars and a lot of gas and dust. Irregular galaxies are usually smaller than other types of galaxies and may grow larger over time.

Although galaxies vary in shape, they are similar in other ways. For example, gravitational forces hold the stars in all galaxies together. Also, all galaxies are in motion. The stars move within the galaxies, and the galaxies move within the universe.

The three categories of galaxies are spiral, elliptical, and irregular. Gravitational forces between stars hold galaxies together.

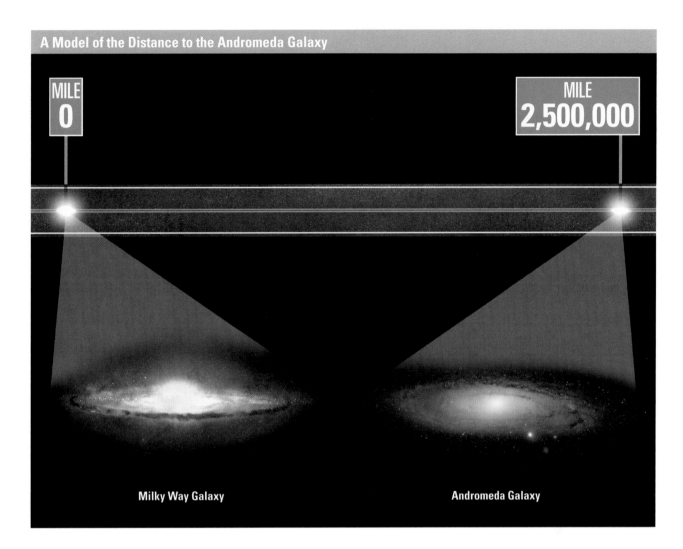

A Model of the Distance to the Andromeda Galaxy

MILE
0

MILE
2,500,000

Milky Way Galaxy

Andromeda Galaxy

4. Modeling Distances Between Galaxies

If you go far from the city lights on a clear, dark night, you can see the Andromeda galaxy with only your eyes. The galaxy looks like a fuzzy star. How does a galaxy that contains almost a trillion stars and is about 200,000 ly across appear no bigger than a single star?

Recall that the moon and sun appear to be the same size because the moon is much closer to Earth than the sun. Similarly, the Andromeda galaxy looks tiny because it is much farther away than the planets and most of the stars that you can see. It is about 2,500,000 ly away. You can use the same scale model, where 1 ly is 1 mile, to understand how far away that would be. It would be a long trip to the Andromeda galaxy.

The distance to the Andromeda galaxy is so far that it is hard to imagine. But that galaxy is one of the closest galaxies to the Milky Way. Scientists have discovered other galaxies more than 13 billion ly away from Earth. How far would this be in your model? 13 billion miles is far enough to go from LA to the sun and back more than 65 times!

Since galaxies are so far away, scientists and engineers have not sent a spacecraft to another one. Scientists who want to study other galaxies use telescopes to collect all their data.

Figure 9.4

The Andromeda galaxy is farther away than any star you can see in the sky. In this model, one light year is represented by one mile. The Andromeda Galaxy would be 2,500,000 miles away from our home, the Milky Way Galaxy.

5. The Universe

You are at a restaurant with your friend and his family, and you are trying to decide what to order. "Get the vegetable lasagna," your friend says, "It is the best lasagna in the universe!"

You hear the word *universe* all the time, but what does it mean? The **universe** is all of space, time, matter, and energy. The universe includes everything that exists. No one knows how big the universe is. It might go on forever, or it might have an edge that is too far away to see. Although astronomers cannot see the whole universe, they assume that the parts they cannot see are similar to the parts that they can see. Like all scientists, astronomers assume that natural systems have consistent and observable patterns.

Before Edwin Hubble's time, the Milky Way was the largest known structure in the universe. People could see a few other galaxies, but they did not know that they were outside of the Milky Way. Hubble discovered that stars beyond the Milky Way existed, and since Hubble's time, telescopes have gotten bigger and better. Scientists use these telescopes to look farther and farther into the universe.

In 2009, scientists released the photo shown, which was taken with the Hubble Space Telescope. Each speck of light in the image is a galaxy millions or billions of light-years away. Edwin Hubble would be amazed at the number of galaxies found by the telescope named after him. And he would be amazed at the size of the universe.

The Hubble Space Telescope took this photo by pointing its cameras at a tiny section of the sky about 0.5 percent of the area of the moon. You can tell that some of the objects in the photo are galaxies. But even the tiny dots that look like stars are distant galaxies.

Scale of Objects in the Universe

Although no one knows how large the universe is, scientists know that it is very, very big. Earth is large on its own, but the solar system is 60,000 times wider than Earth. Though the solar system seems large, the Milky Way galaxy is 200,000,000 times larger than the solar system. The universe is 276,000 times larger than the Milky Way Galaxy.

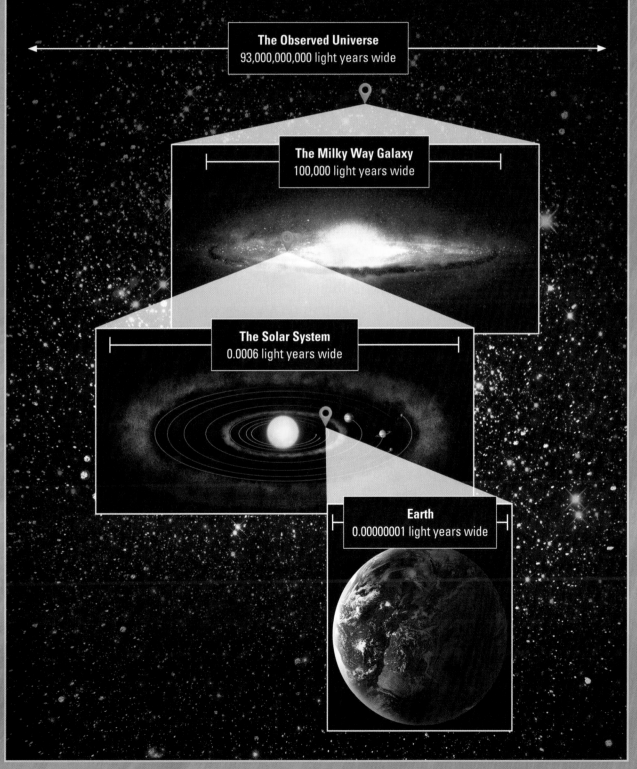

The Observed Universe
93,000,000,000 light years wide

The Milky Way Galaxy
100,000 light years wide

The Solar System
0.0006 light years wide

Earth
0.00000001 light years wide

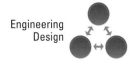

Engineering
Design

6. Engineering Telescopes to See More of the Universe

Edwin Hubble's amazing accomplishments may not have been possible without the work of another American astronomer. As a teenager in the late 1800s, George Ellery Hale already showed a desire to build bigger and more powerful telescopes. What engineering and other obstacles did Hale have to overcome to build the 20th century's most important tools for astronomers?

Two Designs in Competition In 1897, Hale built a 40-inch refracting telescope in Wisconsin, which was the largest refracting telescope ever made. A refracting telescope uses a curved glass lens to focus light to form an image. That lens of Hale's telescope remains the biggest refractor in the world because a piece of glass any larger would change shape under its own weight.

Not satisfied with only the objects a 40-inch refracting telescope could see, Hale turned to a different technology—reflecting telescopes. A reflecting telescope uses one or more curved mirrors to focus light to form an image. Glass factories could make bigger glass bases for mirrors than for lenses. The resulting larger telescopes could gather more light and see more of the universe.

In 1906, Hale had a French company make a large glass disk to form the base of a 100-inch mirror. It took two years and many tries for the engineers to succeed. But finally they produced the biggest piece of cast glass in the world. After a long journey to California, and years of grinding and polishing, the piece of glass became the reflecting mirror for the Hooker telescope, located on Mt. Wilson in southern California. This was the very telescope Hubble used to discover galaxies beyond the Milky Way Galaxy.

Before the 20th century, astronomers used both reflecting and refracting telescopes. By the beginning of the 20th century, George Ellery Hale realized that more powerful telescopes could only be built and designed if they were reflecting telescopes. The Hooker Telescope built by Hale had a 100-inch mirror.

Criteria for a 200-inch Telescope When the 100-inch telescope was completed in 1917, Hale was already looking for funds to design a 200-inch reflecting telescope for another location in California. It would be very expensive, and there were many criteria to meet. The telescope mirror had to hold its shape even as the air temperature changed and as it was moved to view different parts of the sky. It would have to hold the photographic plate, where the image would focus, perfectly still. The controls that move the huge structure would have to take into account the apparent motion of the stars. Furthermore, a 200-inch glass disk would be extremely difficult to produce.

Testing a Process with Scale Models Engineers at a U.S. glass company wanted to use a type of glass they invented to cast the big disk. They cast a 26-inch scale model to test their process. They used their model to test how to build the mold and the precise mixture of glass to use. They also used their model to test how to pour the molten glass, how to keep the disk hot during the pouring, and how to support the ever-increasing weight of the disk. Then they tested how to control the months-long cooling process so that the solid disk would be free of flaws.

Slowly the engineers cast larger and larger models, each time making small changes to improve their process. They had to make sure that a process that worked on a 26-inch scale model would also work on the 200-inch disk that Hale wanted. After testing a 120-inch model, they had optimized the process enough to expect success in making the 200-inch disk.

The disk was ground and installed in the new Hale telescope on Mt. Palomar. Edwin Hubble had the honor of being the first astronomer to use this telescope to take official photos of the sky in 1949. Many discoveries were made with it, including that the size of the universe was at least twice the size of what astronomers had previously thought.

Engineers cast a series of scale models to test their process for producing larger and larger glass disks. The successful 200-inch mirror was installed at Mt. Palomar Observatory. Although Hale had already died, his wife was present at the dedication ceremony.

LESSON SUMMARY

Beyond the Solar Systems

Modeling Distances Between Stars The unit of a light-year is often used to describe the distances between stars. A light-year is the distance that light travels in one year in the vacuum of space.

The Milky Way Galaxy The solar system is in the Milky Way, which is a galaxy that has a disk shape and spiral arms. Stars in the Milky Way galaxy revolve around its center, where a supermassive black hole is located.

Types of Galaxies The three main categories of galaxies are spiral galaxies, elliptical galaxies, and irregular galaxies.

Modeling Distances Between Galaxies Galaxies look tiny in the sky because they are much farther away than any individual star you can see. Scientists use models to understand the distance between the Milky Way and other galaxies.

The Universe The universe contains all matter, energy, time, and space. Nobody knows exactly how large the universe is.

Engineering Telescopes to See More of the Universe Engineers designed telescopes that allow scientists to explore more of the universe. By using scale models, Engineers can test their design before creating a large version.

Is Anyone Out There?

You've seen it in science fiction movies: A character receives a message from aliens outside our solar system. Sometimes the message is friendly and sometimes it is not. In reality, no one has ever received a message from aliens—but not for a lack of listening. Scientists are always listening and hoping to hear something. Do aliens exist, and will humans ever hear from them? Should humans try to contact aliens?

Aliens and *extraterrestrials* are two words used to refer to life from other planets. But not any kind of life could send messages into space; only so-called "intelligent life" could do so. This term usually describes life forms that use language and can understand math and science concepts.

Many scientists think aliens exist because the universe is so vast that it is unlikely that Earth is the only place with life. If there are planets with intelligent life, the chances of hearing from at least one is pretty high. Scientists think that planets outside of our solar system might have intelligent life, but they do not know how many of those planets exist. An equation called the *Drake Equation* helps scientists describe what they would need to know in order to estimate how many planets have intelligent life that could be sending signals through space.

The Drake Equation starts with the number of stars in the Milky Way, which is then multiplied by additional factors such as the fraction of stars that have planets. In total, seven variables are multiplied together to determine how many planets could have intelligent life. The problem with using the Drake Equation is that the values of the variables are not accurately known. So, the "answer" to the Drake Equation can only be an estimate, and the estimates range from one to one million or more.

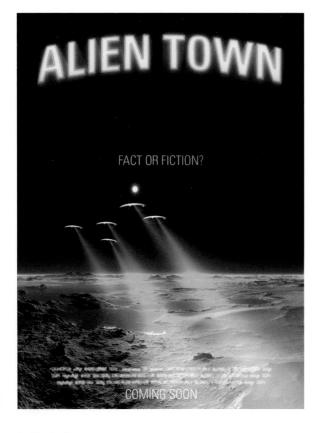

Science fiction movies often show aliens visiting or communicating with people on Earth. In reality, no evidence of intelligent alien life has been found. But scientists continue to try to figure out if there is intelligent life outside our solar system.

We're Listening

Even without knowing the exact answer to the Drake Equation, some scientists are very excited about the possibility of finding intelligent life on other planets. These scientists do research as part of the Search for Extraterrestrial Intelligence (SETI).

SETI looks for aliens by "listening" to radio waves from space. Radio waves are a type of light, but unlike visible light, you cannot see radio waves with your eyes. Humans use radio waves to send information across long distances. SETI scientists think that intelligent aliens may also communicate with radio waves and that aliens may send radio waves across interstellar space. Scientists hope to find radio waves that could have been sent by aliens.

Scientists use radio telescopes to detect radio waves. Radio telescopes look like satellite dishes and sometimes are in a group of several dishes called an *array*. Some SETI scientists use the Allen Telescope Array in Northern California to detect radio waves. SETI scans the skies and space hoping to hear a narrow-band signal, which is a signal spread over only a small range of wavelengths. Radio signals that people on Earth use to communicate are narrow-band signals. Scientists think that narrow-band signals can probably be produced only by artificial means, so a narrow-band signal from space may mean that an intelligent alien society built a machine that produced that signal.

In 1977, SETI detected a narrow-band signal! That signal is now called the "Wow" signal because a scientist wrote "Wow" on the data printout showing the signal. But the "Wow" signal was detected just that once and has never been detected again. Scientists may never know for sure if the signal was sent by aliens, but many hope it was.

Astronomers use radio telescopes to search for signs of intelligent life by listening for narrow-band radio wave signals. The radio telescopes in this image are called the Allen Telescope Array.

Out-Of-This-World Worlds

Scientists have been doing SETI research since the late 1950s. For years, some people thought that the SETI work was misguided. After all, there was no evidence that planets outside of our solar system existed; many people thought that the sun was the only star with planets. How could intelligent life—or any life—exist if no other planets existed in the universe?

After 1995, astronomers no longer had to guess because they discovered the first exoplanet around a star similar to the sun. An *exoplanet* is a planet outside of our solar system. Since then, nearly 5,000 possible exoplanets have been found, and of those, almost 2,000 exoplanets have been at least partially confirmed to exist.

The first exoplanets discovered were large, gas planets that followed orbits that were very close to their stars and were named *hot Jupiters*. Hot Jupiters are the easiest kind of exoplanet to find because they are so large and their orbital periods are so short. However, scientists (particularly SETI scientists) are even more interested in trying to find *twin Earths*, or Earth-like exoplanets where life may have developed on them similar to the way life developed on Earth. They want to find terrestrial planets about the size of Earth that have orbits within their stars' Habitable Zone.

The Habitable Zone, also called the Goldilocks Zone, is an area around a star that might be just right for life. If a planet with an atmosphere is in this zone, the temperature of the planet is not too hot and not too cold. It is the right temperature to have liquid water on its surface. Liquid water is important because scientists believe that it is necessary for life. Although scientists have found several possible twin Earths, they currently do not have a way to find out if life exists on those planets. For now, they can only identify exoplanets for future research.

Meanwhile, the discovery of all exoplanets is helping SETI scientists get better estimates for the answer to the Drake Equation. Two factors in the Drake Equation are the fraction of stars that have planets and the number of planets per solar system in the Goldilocks Zone. Exoplanet studies will improve the estimates for these factors.

Exoplanets are planets outside of our solar system. Thousands of exoplanets have been found. Scientists hope to find twin Earths, which are planets similar to Earth that may have developed life as Earth did.

Hey, We're Over Here!

For the most part, SETI work has been passive: listening for signals and looking for exoplanets. Some scientists want to do more active SETI work. Active SETI means sending messages into space in hopes that they will be detected by an intelligent alien civilization.

Active SETI for Now There are four spacecraft heading out of our solar system, and they each carry messages. Pioneer 10 and 11, launched by NASA, each have a gold plaque with images etched on them that show what humans look like and where Earth is located. Voyager 1 and 2 have gold records on them that can be played to produce sounds and images from Earth. The records also include information on where Earth is. However, these four spacecraft are traveling very slowly and are unlikely to be found by aliens any time soon.

The fastest way to send a message to extraterrestrials is to use light waves, like radio waves or visible light. Scientists who favor active SETI think that humans should send messages using electromagnetic waves. In fact, some messages have already been sent using electromagnetic waves such as radio waves.

The most famous radio wave message sent into space is the Arecibo Message. This message was broadcast for three minutes in 1974 from the Arecibo Radio Telescope in Puerto Rico. When translated correctly, the message produces an image. The top of the image shows a code for the numbers 1 through 10. The other parts of the image describes DNA, a molecule found in all living things on Earth, a scientific stick figure of a human, a map of our solar system, and a drawing of the Arecibo Telescope. No one has yet answered the message.

Active SETI in the Future? Although some people want to send more messages like the Arecibo Message, people who oppose active SETI do not. Active SETI opponents, some of whom are distinguished scientists, think sending messages could be dangerous because no one knows who might receive the messages. At best, the messages could be received by friendly aliens who happily share advanced technology with us. At worst, warrior aliens could receive the message and come to Earth to destroy all life on the planet.

Scientists on both sides of the active SETI debate do agree that humans should continue to look and listen for life on other planets. They would like to learn for certain that we are not alone. ◆

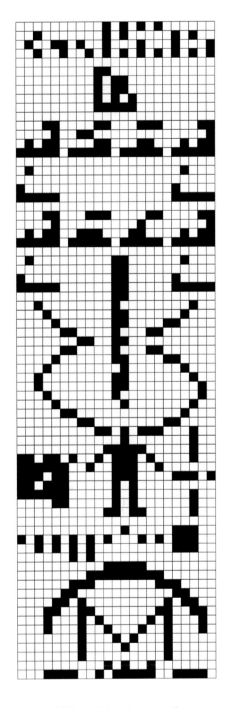

Active SETI work involves sending messages into space for aliens to hear. The Arecibo Message is a famous active SETI message. The translated message produces the image shown here depicting information about human life on Earth.

Learning Resources

The whole Earth and everything beyond it is the subject of science. This set of learning resources includes some essential thinking tools you need in order to explore, investigate, and explain how the world works.

Laboratory Safety

To think like a scientist, you have to act like one. This means making observations, experimenting, and carrying out other types of investigations. The same goes for solving engineering problems. You have to propose, build, test, and improve your designed solutions. All of these things are fun and interesting, but there can be risks involved in handling equipment and materials. What do you have to be aware of to stay safe when practicing science and engineering?

Your teacher may ask you to sign a Science Safety Contract and discuss it with your parents. This is an important first step towards science safety. Before working in the science lab, review these rules.

☑ Understand the hazards and rules for a particular investigation before you begin.

☑ Make sure your personal clothing is safe for the lab. Do not wear loose clothing, especially long sleeves.

☑ Wear closed shoes to protect your feet.

☑ If you have long hair, tie it back.

☑ Wear safety goggles, protective aprons, and gloves when required by your teacher.

☑ Transport and handle all equipment and chemicals as directed by your teacher.

☑ Report breaks, spills, or other accidents to your teacher right away.

☑ Report injuries to your teacher right away, and follow your school's first aid procedures.

☑ Know where safety equipment is in the lab you use and when or how to use it.

☑ Dispose of materials in the designated containers at the end of the investigation.

☑ Clean up your work area and wash your hands at the conclusion of the investigation.

☑ Know what to do in case of a hazardous event such as a power failure, earthquake, or emergency evacuation.

☑ Be aware of safety for everyone in your group.

Planning Investigations

Designing your own investigations is a chance to act like a real scientist—and that includes keeping yourself and others safe.

☑ Choose equipment and materials that your teacher tells you are safe to use.

☑ Plan how you will handle the materials safely, including how you will dispose of materials that cannot be used again.

☑ Include safety steps when writing your procedure.

☑ Always obtain permission from your teacher before carrying out your investigation plan.

Field Trip Safety

Some of the most important thigs you can do to stay safe on a field trip is to be prepared in advance.

☑ Return a signed parental permission form to your teacher before a field trip.

☑ Check the weather forecast so that you can choose appropriate clothing. If there is any possibility of severe weather, make sure there is a plan for taking shelter.

☑ No matter the weather, wear footwear that encloses and protects your feet.

☑ Wear clothing, hats, or sunscreen to protect yourself from sunburn. Remember, you can get burned on a cloudy day as well as on a sunny one.

☑ Learn in advance the types of organisms you may encounter that are dangerous and should be avoided.

☑ During the field trip, don't touch plants unless instructed by your teacher or guide.

☑ Know how to get first aid for poisonous plants and animal stings and bites.

☑ Never eat or put in your mouth anything you find outdoors without permission.

☑ Wash up carefully after an outdoor science activity.

☑ If the area you visited has ticks, inspect your clothing and body for ticks at the end of the field trip.

Safety for Living Things in the Classroom

When you investigate living things, you can't just think about yourself. You have to think about the organisms in your care, too.

☑ Understand appropriate and humane treatment of animals. This includes selecting a suitable container to house the animals and making sure the temperature is within the proper range for that species.

☑ Help make sure that animals kept in the science classroom are provided with adequate water, food, and that their containers are kept clean.

☑ Keep handling of animals to a minimum and never disturb sleeping animals.

☑ Plan for appropriate care of living things over weekends, holidays, and vacations.

☑ Don't bring personal pets or unknown plants or animals into school, as they may be poisonous, venomous, or negatively affect the other living things in your science classroom.

☑ Never carry out investigations that will cause discomfort, pain, or disease to animals.

☑ Return native wild species to their natural environment.

☑ Never release non-native species into the natural environment.

☑ Wash your hands and surfaces after handling living things.

Asking Questions

Asking questions is central to science. Scientists learn about the natural world by asking questions and trying to answer them. As scientists learn about the natural world, they come up with more questions to answer. What kinds of questions do scientists ask, and how can you learn to ask them?

Questions drive the scientific process. Scientists ask testable questions to guide their research and gain scientific knowledge. This knowledge can lead to new questions to be answered.

Questions Scientists ask questions about the natural world and about current scientific ideas. The types of questions scientists might ask include: What causes a particular phenomenon? How do different factors affect observations? Why did an event occur?

Testability Science can only answer questions that are testable, which means that a scientist must be able to gather evidence to answer the question. To determine if a question is testable, ask yourself: How can the answer to this question be determined? Would the answer be a fact or an opinion? Can I design an investigation to answer this question?

Phenomena or theories

Testability

Science Testable questions can lead to new scientific knowledge, which can lead to new questions. Ask yourself: How can I gather data to answer this question? How well does this data support the answer? Are there other possible answers that this data could support?

Phenomena and Theories Scientists ask questions based on observed phenomena and scientific theories. The questions may be asked to clarify ideas or to introduce new ideas. Ask yourself: What other questions does this new understanding raise? How does this explanation relate to other scientific ideas or theories?

If you go to cities around the world, you will probably see a couple of pigeons or maybe a couple of hundreds of pigeons. Unlike many other wild animals, pigeons do not seem to mind living around people. How might you research pigeons to find out why that is?

Asking Questions You can start your research by asking questions. These questions might include: Why are pigeons more common in cities than other species of birds? What birds lived in an area before an area was developed? How does the diet of a city pigeon compare with the diet of a pigeon living in the country?

You can ask testable questions to learn about the natural environment. For example, if you are studying pigeons, you might ask questions to compare the diet of city pigeons with the diet of country pigeons.

Determining Testability After scientists come up with questions, they pick at least one question to investigate further. Suppose that you wanted to find the answer to the question "How does the diet of a city pigeon compare with the diet of a pigeon living in the country?" The question you are trying to answer must be testable. To determine this, you might ask: What kind of investigation will help answer the question? What evidence do I have to gather to answer the question?

Conducting Science You may want to start your investigation on pigeon diets by reviewing research done by other scientists. Some questions you may consider are: What other research has been done on pigeon diets? What methods did other scientists use? How will my investigation differ or improve on previous investigations?

Coming Up with Phenomena and Theories While investigating pigeon diets, you may try to connect your observations with known phenomena and theories. Ask yourself: What do my observations say about pigeon nutrition? How does a pigeon's diet compare with that of other species of birds? How do my results relate to phenomena like the adaptation of pigeons to their environment?

The fact that asking questions in science often leads to new questions may seem frustrating, but it is actually a good thing. The cycle of questions leading to more questions means that science will always grow and improve.

Defining Problems

Before engineers can begin designing a solution, they have to define the problem they are trying to solve. By thoroughly defining the problem, engineers know exactly what qualities the solution must have and what obstacles they may need to work around to achieve the solution. What do engineers have to do to define a problem?

Defining problems involves clearly identifying the problem, the boundaries and components of the problem, and the criteria and constraints of the problem's solution.

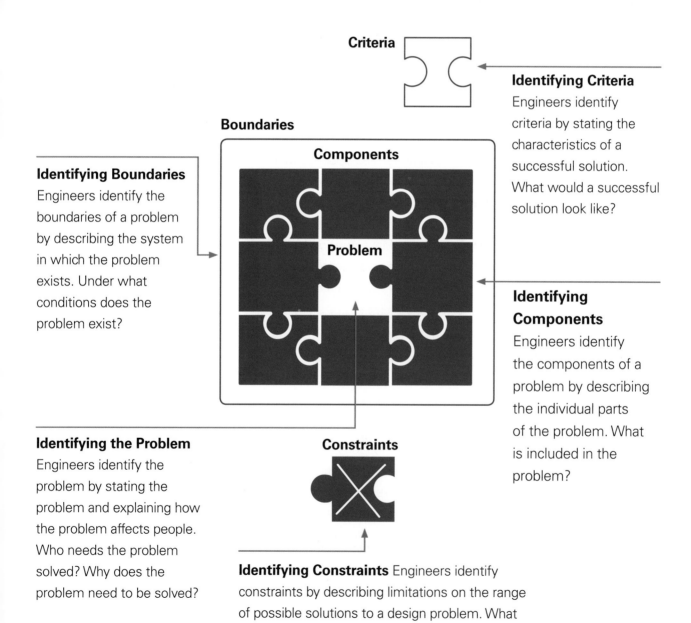

Criteria

Identifying Criteria
Engineers identify criteria by stating the characteristics of a successful solution. What would a successful solution look like?

Boundaries

Components

Identifying Boundaries
Engineers identify the boundaries of a problem by describing the system in which the problem exists. Under what conditions does the problem exist?

Problem

Identifying Components
Engineers identify the components of a problem by describing the individual parts of the problem. What is included in the problem?

Identifying the Problem
Engineers identify the problem by stating the problem and explaining how the problem affects people. Who needs the problem solved? Why does the problem need to be solved?

Constraints

Identifying Constraints Engineers identify constraints by describing limitations on the range of possible solutions to a design problem. What would make a solution impractical or unusable?

Defining a problem by identifying boundaries, components, criteria, and constraints is the first step in finding a good solution. Making healthy lunches that students will eat is a problem that many schools struggle with.

If you could buy anything to eat at your school cafeteria, what would you get? You probably want foods like pizza and cake. But pizza, cake, and other popular foods tend not to be healthy. What can school cafeterias do to encourage students to eat better foods?

Identifying the Problem Kids across the country eat most of their lunches at school. School cafeterias try to provide nutritious meals, but often the healthy parts of the meals end up in the trash. So, the problem is providing healthy foods that students will eat.

Identifying the Boundaries and Components The boundaries of this problem surround the school and the people in it. The components of the problem include the food, the students, school kitchen, kitchen staff, and administrators. The students eat the food that is prepared by the kitchen staff, while the administrators purchase the food and approve the meals. However, many things are not important to the problem, such as the color of the walls and whether lunch tables have chairs or benches to sit on.

Identifying Criteria and Constraints The criteria and constraints of a successful solution can be organized in a table.

Criteria	Constraints
• meals are nutritious	• budget (need to afford food)
• at least 85% of students eat the meal	• kitchen (need right equipment to prepare food)
• meal plan has variety	• time to prepare food

Solving the problem of serving healthy school lunches is not easy, but understanding the problem will help find a solution. If the solution is successful, it will be good and delicious.

Developing and Using Models

Scientists use models to explain and understand natural phenomena. Scientific models can be physical models such as a globe or a drawing of a cell. Scientific models can also be conceptual models, which means that they are collections of related ideas. For example, the big bang theory is a conceptual model to describe how the universe began. How can you learn to develop models the way a scientist would?

When scientists develop a model, they identify the components of the model, describe the relationship between the components, and explain the connections between the model and the real world.

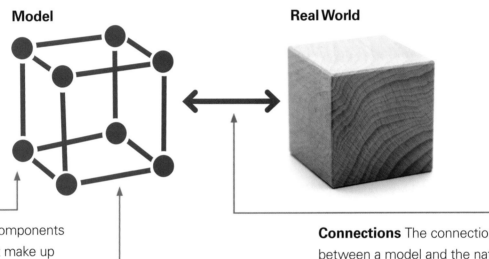

Model

Real World

Components Components are the parts that make up the model. Each component represents something in the real world. When you develop a model, you have to decide which parts of the real word are important to represent and which are not.

Relationships The relationships in a model describe how the components interact. When you develop a model, the relationships you describe help you understand how the components of the model work together and make predictions about the model.

Connections The connections between a model and the natural phenomenon it represents make the model useful. Models simplify the phenomenon to make it easier to observe, understand, predict, or quantify.

Scientists develop some models by combining what they have learned about a particular phenomenon. However, sometimes scientists use a simple, common object as a model to help explain something in nature. For example, lasagna could be used as a model for sedimentary rock. The common object used as a model has some similar features to the phenomenon it is modeling, but it generally cannot explain everything about the phenomenon. How is lasagna a good model for sedimentary rock formation, and how does it fall short?

Components The layers of lasagna represent the layers of rock in sedimentary rock. The different layers in lasagna—noodle, cheese, and meat—can represent different kinds of rock.

Relationships Lasagna layers are distinct, so you can see each layer. One relationship in this model is the order of the layers. Using this relationship, you can see how the lasagna was built even if you did not see it being assembled. You know the lasagna was built up so that the first layer is at the bottom and the last layer is at the top.

Scientists develop models to explain or describe natural phenomena. Lasagna is a useful model for describing the structure and formation of sedimentary rock, but it cannot compare in terms of timescale.

Connections The structure of the lasagna and the way it was built are similar to the structure and the formation of sedimentary rock. The layers in sedimentary rock are distinct and easy to see. Sedimentary rock is also built up with the oldest rock layers at the bottom and the newest rock layers at the top.

However, lasagna and sedimentary rock have important differences. A person can build a lasagna in about 15 minutes, but sedimentary rock may take millions of years to build up. Studying the layers in sedimentary rock can tell you about the environments in which the layers formed. Studying lasagna layers cannot tell you much of anything, except for which layer you like the best!

Planning and Carrying Out Investigations

Scientific research involves conducting investigations. Scientists use many different methods for planning investigations, but every method has common elements. One method is outlined here. The elements in this method are common to other methods that a scientist might use. What things should you consider when planning an investigation, and what might happen when carrying out an investigation?

The steps in planning and carrying out an investigation can happen in any order and can be repeated multiple times.

Identifying Evidence Identify what evidence you need to answer your question; only some evidence will be useful. If you were investigating why birds sing in the morning, you might observe birds in the morning and also at other times of the day to see what else they do.

Identifying the Phenomenon
The subject of your investigation might be a phenomenon to be explained, a question to be answered, or a design to be tested. You might try to answer the question, "Why do birds sing in the morning?"

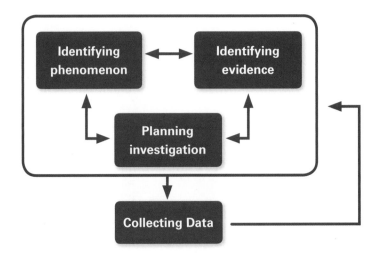

Planning the Investigation
Describe how you will gather data that will serve as evidence toward a claim. Create a specific list of steps to follow. For example, you could set up a camera in a park. Then, you could watch the video, marking down bird activity such as singing, feeding, and flying.

Collecting Data Collect your data by following the steps outlined in your investigation plan. Be sure to keep your data organized. For an investigation about birds singing, you could make a table with rows marked with time of day and columns marked with various bird behaviors.

Refining the Plan Refining your investigation plan means making changes to improve it. Ask yourself questions such as: Was the data accurately and precisely collected? Does the data support a claim about the phenomenon that I am investigating? If the answers are "no," then you need to change the investigation's plan.

Your science class is having a toy car race to investigate forces and motion. Each team of students is given a kit with which to build a toy car, but the design of each car is up to the team members. What plan do you come up with for your investigation?

Identifying the Phenomenon Together your class brainstorms factors that may affect the speed of a toy car. The class decides to investigate how a car's shape affects the car's speed.

Identifying Evidence Your class identifies the data to collect: which car shape wins each race. These data can then be analyzed to find evidence for which shape is best for a fast car.

Specifying the Steps The class comes up with the following steps:

1. Each of the 15 teams will make a car, and each car will have a different shape.

2. Cars will race on a track that has five lanes.

3. In preliminary rounds, five cars will race at least two times. The first car to win twice will advance to the final round.

4. In the final round, the preliminary round winners will race. The first car to win twice will be declared the best shape.

Collecting Data The winners of the preliminary rounds include your wedge-shaped car, a minivan-shaped car, and a car shaped like a cone. However, you notice that the car in the leftmost lane always finishes last.

Scientists plan and carry out investigations to gather evidence to support their explanations. You can gather evidence about which toy car design is fastest by holding a series of races and recording which design wins each race.

Refining the Plan Because the leftmost car always loses, the answer to the question, "Were the data accurately collected?" is "no." The class runs trial races, which show that cars run slower in the outside lanes. The class revises the investigation plan. Instead of racing five cars, you race three cars using only the center lanes. Then you will have two semifinal rounds and one final round.

Your wedge-shaped car wins its preliminary round and its semifinal before barely losing to the cone-shaped car in the final round. The race is so close that some classmates think the investigation may need more revision to be sure of the winning design. What other revisions could you make?

Analyzing and Interpreting Data

Scientists and engineers collect data in many different ways. In order to connect data to their investigation, scientists and engineers have to analyze and interpret the data. How can you think like a scientist or an engineer to make sense of data you collect?

Analyzing and interpreting data involves organizing the data, identifying relationships within the data, and then interpreting the data based on the relationships found.

Organizing Data Scientists and engineers organize their data in tables or graphs to help them make sense of it. Data that include written descriptions might be organized in data tables, while data that show changes over time might be organized in a line graph, bar graph, or pie chart.

Identifying Relationships Scientists and engineers identify relationships by looking for patterns in the organized data. They ask themselves questions such as: What parts of the data show changes? Are there data that change in regular ways? Do two different kinds of data change in similar ways?

Interpreting Data Scientists and engineers interpret data by drawing conclusions from the relationships identified. They may ask: What could be causing the patterns in the data? What could happen if the patterns continue? Could the patterns have more than one explanation?

Your science class is studying a nearby lake. You collect measurements of air and water temperature at the same place at the same time every day for a year.

Organizing Data You divide the measurements into air temperatures and water temperatures for each month. Then you find the average air temperature and water temperature for each month. Finally, you organize the average temperatures into a data table.

Both air temperature and water temperature change throughout the year. But you are not sure how the temperature changes are related. So, you graph the temperatures over time.

Identifying Relationships You can see a relationship between air and water temperature in the graph. The changes in temperatures follow similar patterns, but the patterns do not line up. The water graph is about a month behind the air graph. The air graph reaches its highest temperature in July, but the water graph does not reach its highest temperature until August.

Interpreting Data After studying your graph, you propose an explanation for why air and water temperatures follow a similar pattern. You propose that the changing air temperatures cause changes in water temperature. That is why the temperature changes follow similar patterns. Furthermore, you suggest the patterns do not line up because water changes temperature slower than air does.

The data in this table are organized using a line graph. You can see a relationship in the data on the graph; the changes in air and water temperature follow a similar pattern. How would you interpret this relationship?

Average Lake Air and Water Temperatures

Month	Air Temp. (°C)	Water Temp. (°C)
Jan (1)	-5.6	6.1
Feb (2)	-4.4	3.3
Mar (3)	-1.1	1.7
Apr (4)	7.2	2.2
May (5)	12.2	3.3
June (6)	18.3	6.7
July (7)	21.1	10.0
Aug (8)	17.8	16.7
Sept (9)	12.8	15.6
Oct (10)	4.4	13.9
Nov (11)	-0.6	10.0
Dec (12)	-2.2	7.8

Using Mathematical and Computational Thinking

Scientists use mathematical and computational thinking in many ways. They might use math to analyze data, make predictions, or build scientific models. Furthermore, some scientific laws and principles can be expressed as equations. For example, Newton's second law of motion can be expressed as force = mass × acceleration. In each of these situations, scientists use math to represent observed systems. How can you use math to represent systems you encounter in science and your everyday life?

When scientists use math to describe a system, they state what parts of the system are represented, describe how numbers and symbols are used to model the system, and then use math to analyze the system.

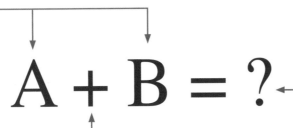

Representation In math, representation means to use symbols (such as letters) to stand in for variables in a system. For example, Newton's law describes the relationship between three variables: force, mass, and acceleration. These variables are represented by the letters F, m, and a, respectively.

Mathematical Modeling Mathematical modeling means to find how the variables in a system are related mathematically. For example, the relationship between the variables in Newton's second law is represented mathematically by the equation $F = m \times a$. You could use graphs to find relationships or you could see if the variables are related by an equation. Scientists sometimes build computer simulations that connect many different variables.

Analysis Analyzing a mathematical system means to find patterns in the system. The pattern can be used to make predictions or support claims. Analyzing a system might involve solving equations, finding trends in graphs, or using a computer simulation. For example, you can use the equation for Newton's second law to analyze how a change in force affects acceleration. If a force on an object is doubled, the acceleration of the object will also double.

The equation for Newton's second law of motion, like many equations in science, can be applied in many situations. However, scientists sometimes develop equations that describe only the situation that they are studying. How can you develop an equation to describe the change in a rabbit population in an ecosystem?

Representation The first step in developing a rabbit population equation is to identify and represent the variables in the system. You might pick the following variables and representations:

- *b* represents the number of rabbits born

- *e* represents the number of rabbits eaten by predators

- *d* represents the number of rabbits that died of natural causes

- Δp represents the change in rabbit population (The Greek letter delta (Δ) often means "change in," so Δp means change in *p*, the rabbit population.)

Mathematical Modeling To mathematically model the change in rabbit population, you have to decide how each variable affects the population. Does the variable increase or decrease the population? What mathematical operations are the equivalents to increasing and decreasing a value? An increase in population would add to the population, and a decrease would subtract from the population. Births increase the population and deaths decrease the population. So an equation for the change in population would be:

$$\Delta p = b - e - d$$

Scientists often use math to represent the systems they are studying. An equation can be used to find the change in a rabbit population in an ecosystem. The equation can be analyzed to predict how the rabbit population might change under various conditions.

Analysis To analyze the accuracy of your equation, you might solve the equation to see how the number of rabbits changes each month. Then you might draw conclusions, such as the rabbit population increases in the summer months due to a rise in births. You could also analyze the equation by using it to make predictions. What would happen if the predators in the ecosystem died? What would happen if a disease spread throughout the rabbit population?

Constructing Explanations

As they work, scientists construct explanations of phenomena. Constructing explanations is similar to engaging in argument from evidence but has key differences. When scientists engage in argument, they are using evidence to defend an idea. When scientists construct explanations, they are using evidence and reasoning to build an idea. How can you learn to think like a scientist when constructing explanations for the phenomena you experience?

Scientists construct explanations by using reasoning to describe the connections between phenomena and evidence.

Phenomenon When scientists construct explanations, the phenomenon is the event or observation that they are explaining. For example, scientists might try to explain why honeybees are dying off.

Arguments for the Explanation Scientists use arguments to support their explanation. An argument is made up of a claim, evidence for that claim, and reasons why the evidence supports the claim. For example, scientists might claim that more flowering plants are sprayed with pesticides now than ever before. Evidence supporting that claim may include data about historic and present day sales of pesticides.

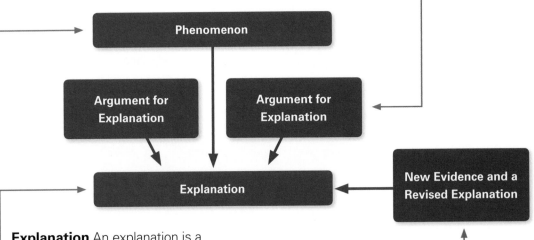

Explanation An explanation is a statement composed of one or more arguments that describe how or why the phenomenon happens. An example explanation might be: Honeybees are dying off because of the use of pesticides on flowering plants.

New Evidence and a Revised Explanation After scientists have proposed an explanation, new evidence may arise that makes the scientists change their explanation. Perhaps scientists studying honeybees learn that a disease is spreading throughout honeybee populations. They may revise their explanation to include the disease as a reason why the bees are dying off.

You can construct explanations for phenomena that you observe in your everyday life. For example, suppose you have a banana bread recipe that you make successfully all the time. Your friend who lives in Denver, Colorado tries to make the bread, but the batter overflows and the bread is gummy. What causes the differences?

Phenomenon Your friend says that he followed your recipe exactly. You determine that the only variable that changed between your loaf and his loaf was where the loaves were made. So, the phenomenon that you are trying to explain is why the same recipe produces a nice loaf at your home but makes a mess at your friend's.

Explanation You and your friend talk to figure out the differences between your homes. You know some differences, such as the number of bedrooms in the homes, will not cause changes in how bread bakes. You rule out those differences as factors. Eventually, you come up with an explanation. The recipe failed because your friend in Denver lives at a higher altitude than you do.

Arguments for the Explanation The main argument for your explanation is that the higher altitude in Denver causes the banana bread batter to rise too much during the baking process. You learned that the air pressure at higher altitudes is lower. When the air pressure that is pushing down on the batter is lower, the air bubbles produced by the baking soda in the batter can get bigger. The bigger bubbles cause the batter to rise too much and overflow the pan.

New Evidence and a Revised Explanation You tell your friend your explanation, and he has another idea. He explains that the lower pressure in Denver allows liquids to evaporate more quickly. This new evidence causes you to rethink your explanation.

Your explanation is not completely wrong, but it needs to be improved. Your explanation accounts for the batter overflowing but does not explain why the loaf was gummy. You cut yourself a piece of banana bread while you think about how quicker evaporation of liquid in the batter might affect the bread's texture. Hopefully, the snack will help you come up with a more complete explanation!

Scientists construct explanations of phenomena and use arguments to support their explanations. An explanation as to why a banana bread recipe fails in Denver is that the city is at a higher altitude. Therefore, Denver has a lower air pressure.

Designing Solutions

An engineer's primary job is to design solutions to problems. You use these solutions all the time. For example, an engineer designed the calculator you use in math class. Engineers have also designed bus routes, airplane seats, and water treatment plants. How do engineers come up with their solutions? And how do they know which solution is best?

Engineers generate a lot of ideas for solutions. They then narrow down those solutions to find the best one to a given problem.

Possible Solutions Engineers think of many different solutions to a single problem. All the possible solutions should be based on scientific knowledge. They may ask themselves: What scientific ideas are related to the problem? What scientific ideas will help or hinder finding a solution to this problem?

Evaluating Solutions Evaluating solutions is the process of comparing the solutions to the criteria and the constraints. In this step, engineers determine how well each solution meets the criteria and fits within the constraints.

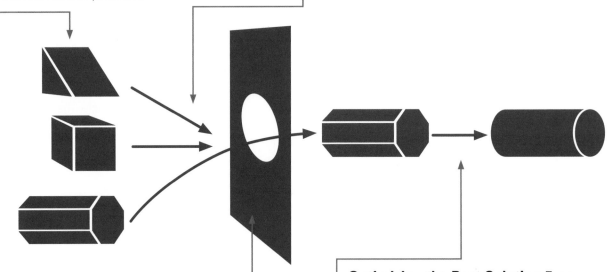

Criteria and Constraints Criteria are the requirements that must be met for an engineering solution to be successful. Constraints are limitations on an engineering solution. Criteria and constraints describe which possible solutions are good and which are not as good. Criteria and constraints may be redefined based on things learned during the designing process.

Optimizing the Best Solution Even after picking the best solution to a problem, engineers need to refine the solution. During this step, engineers test their solution and make changes based on the results of the tests. The solution may need to go through several iterations to make it the best possible solution.

Suppose that your class is having a fundraiser, and the class decides to sell cookie cutters in the shape of the school's logo. Before you can sell the cutters, you have to make them. And before you make the cutters, you have to decide what material to use.

Criteria and Constraints The criteria for the material include that it has to have the ability to be shaped in the form of your school's logo, and it has to hold its shape. Other criteria are that the material has to be able to cut cookie dough and last a long time.

Some of the constraints for the material are that the students in your class have to be able to make the cutter from the material and that the material is not too expensive.

Possible Solutions Science can help you come up with possible materials to use for the cookie cutters. Copper is a possible material because it is a malleable metal. It can be bent into the right shape. Stainless steel is another malleable metal.

Evaluating Solutions You use the criteria and constraints to evaluate the solutions. Copper fits the following criteria: It can be shaped, it can hold its shape, and it will last a long time. It fits the constraint that students can shape it, but it is relatively expensive. So, it does not fit within the inexpensive constraint. Stainless steel fits the following criteria: It can be shaped, it can hold its shape, and it will last a long time. It fits within the constraints that students can shape it, and it is inexpensive. You decide to use stainless steel.

Optimizing the Best Solution Using stainless steel, you make a prototype cookie cutter. The prototype is made out of a 1-cm wide strip of steel. You make cookies using the prototype and find that it does not hold its shape. The narrow strip bends too easily.

You make a second prototype that is made out of a 2.5-cm wide strip of steel. You test the second prototype and find that it holds its shape well. This prototype is determined to have the best design.

You and your classmates make 200 cookie cutters that are identical to the second prototype. You sell the cutters and raise enough money for a field trip to a science museum.

Engineers compare solutions to the criteria and constraints to determine which solution is most likely to solve the problem. The best solution is then optimized through testing and refining. You can use a similar process when designing your own solutions.

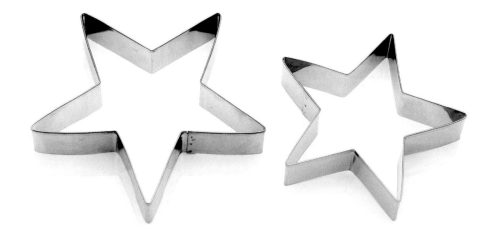

Engaging in Argument from Evidence

Engaging in argument is a key element of scientific practice. However, the arguments that scientists and engineers have with each other are not like typical arguments. They are not trying just to prove each other wrong. Rather, they are trying to collaboratively find the best explanation or model, or design the best solution. What kinds of thinking and statements are needed for a strong argument?

Strong scientific arguments have three key components—a claim, evidence for that claim, and reasoning as to why the evidence supports the claim.

Claim The claim is the statement that the argument is attempting to convince people to believe. Scientists might make claims about an explanation of a phenomenon, such as why snowflakes are always symmetrical. Or, they may make claims about a model, such as a food web. Engineers might make claims about which material is best for their design.

CLAIM

Reasoning
Reasoning
Reasoning

Evidence
Evidence
Evidence

Reasoning Evidence alone is not enough to convince people of a claim. Reasoning shows how the evidence is connected to the claim, using logic or scientific concepts. The reasoning might, for example, explain why a diagram of the structure of water molecules supports the claim that all snowflakes are symmetric.

Evidence Evidence is the data or observations that support a claim. Relevant measurements, tables, and graphs can often be used as strong evidence for a claim. Generally, the more evidence there is for a claim, the stronger the argument is.

Refutation Of course, no argument is one sided. There is often an opportunity for someone to refute an argument. A refutation provides new evidence, which, along with reasoning, shows that the claim is incorrect. A refutation may also provide a different interpretation of the evidence, showing that it does not support the original claim.

Your friend Jerome sent you a photo with his phone. "Check out this great rainbow!" Look at Jerome's photo, and make an argument about the weather Jerome is experiencing. Try asking yourself questions as you develop your argument.

To make your claim, ask yourself, "What kind of weather is in this photo?" Next, identify your evidence by asking, "What specific things do I see in this photo that support my claim?" Then develop your reasoning by asking, "How do the things I pointed out as evidence support my claim?" Your argument might look something like this:

Claim Jerome took the photo while weather was clearing up after a rainstorm.

Evidence There are no visible raindrops in the photo, and the ground does not look wet. However, there is a rainbow in the sky. There are also dark clouds on the right side of the sky, but not on the left side of the sky.

Reasoning Since there are no visible raindrops in the photo and the ground does not look wet, it was probably not raining right when the photo was taken. However, rainbows only form when there are water drops in the sky, and usually form immediately after it has been raining. Also, dark clouds like the ones in the photo usually produce rain. But since the clouds only cover half of the sky in the photograph, the storm seems to be moving away from the place the photograph was taken.

Do you agree with this argument? If not, come up with a refutation. Then, the next time you make a claim, do it like a scientist or engineer—back it up with evidence and reasoning.

Your friend sends you a photo of a rainbow. You can develop an argument of what the weather was like at the moment the photo was taken by asking yourself a set of questions.

Obtaining, Evaluating, and Communicating Information

Scientists spend a lot of time obtaining, evaluating, and communicating information. In fact, most people use this process every day. For example, when you read, you are obtaining information. You then evaluate the information you read by determining if it is accurate and important. You also might communicate this information by talking about it with a friend. How does obtaining, evaluating, and communicating information help scientists do their work?

A scientist may obtain, evaluate, and communicate information during any point in an investigation.

Obtaining Information
When scientists gather information, they may ask: Where can we find information about this topic? What different kinds of information are available?

Evaluating Information
Scientists evaluate information by asking questions like these: What does this information mean? Is this information reliable? Is this information relevant?

Communicating Information Before scientists share information, they must decide how to communicate it. They may ask themselves: What is the best way to communicate this information? Should we give lectures, or should we write about it? Should we make a video? Or will a graph, photo, or mathematical equation better communicate the information?

Although scientific research is generally thought of as being a good thing, it can be controversial. One controversial topic in astronomy is the placement of telescopes on a dormant volcano in Hawaii named Mauna Kea. Some of the world's best telescopes are already on Mauna Kea. Astronomers consider the volcano to be one of the best places in the world for telescopes, and they would like to build additional ones there. However, some Hawaiians consider the volcano to be sacred and do not want any more telescopes built on it. Do you think astronomers should put more telescopes on Mauna Kea? How would you decide?

People obtain, evaluate, and communicate information all the time. Scientists and the public need to obtain and evaluate reliable information when making decisions on controversial topics, such as the placement of telescopes on Mauna Kea.

Obtaining Information *Where can you find information about this topic?* Probably the easiest place for you to get information is the Internet. You can also check specialized resources at the library. *What different kinds of information are available?* Scientists, the Hawaiian government, and Hawaiian residents are some of the groups that provide information on this topic.

Evaluating Information *What does this information mean?* Some information will tell you why Mauna Kea is such a great place for telescopes, while other information will explain the negative impact of telescopes on the volcano. *Is this information reliable?* Consider where the information is from. Websites from universities, the government, and major media outlets tend to be reliable sources. *Is this information relevant?* Once you have information from reliable sources, think about whether the information supports either side of the Mauna Kea controversy. If the information does not help one side or the other, the information is probably not relevant.

Communicating Information *What is the best way to communicate this information?* If you are communicating your opinion about telescopes on Mauna Kea to your class, you might make a poster or explain your reasoning in a class discussion. But if you are a Hawaiian citizen, you might want to write a letter to the state governor that could influence the future of Mauna Kea.

Patterns

Patterns play a key role in many scientific investigations. Scientists make sense of data they have collected by trying to recognize and analyze patterns. Often, noticing a pattern in nature will spark a series of questions. All patterns have an underlying cause, which can be uncovered by a scientific investigation. What patterns can you recognize in the following natural phenomena?

How can the different patterns in finches' beaks help you understand how a species can adapt to its environment? When Charles Darwin discovered different species of finches on the Galapagos Islands, he noticed that each species had a beak that was well-suited to its diet. The differently shaped beaks led Darwin to discover the pattern that exists between the shape of a finch's beak and its individual diet. This pattern seemed to point to a species' ability to adapt to its environment.

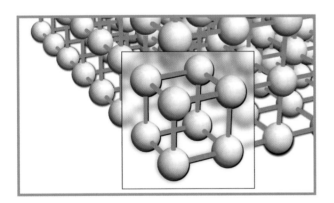

How is the microscopic pattern of table salt related to the macroscopic, or easily visible, shape of a salt crystal? You can see that each individual crystal has a cube-like structure. On the atomic level, sodium and chlorine atoms are arranged in a regular, repeating pattern that is shaped like a cube. The way a substance appears to the human eye is often determined by its atomic level structure.

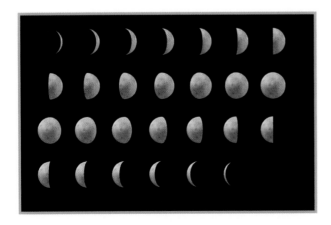

How can understanding patterns help you predict the different shapes of lunar phases? The apparent shape of the moon from Earth is determined by the positions of Earth, the moon, and the sun. Over the course of about a month, the moon transitions from a new moon to a full moon and back to a new moon in a repeating pattern. Because the apparent change in the moon's shape always follows the same pattern, you can predict when the next full moon will take place!

Cause and Effect

Looking for cause-and-effect relationships can help immensely when you are designing experiments to answer scientific questions or testing engineering solutions. Think about these three questions from different areas of science. What experiments might people design to test them?

Do magnetic fields cause compass needles to rotate? Suppose you measure the direction a compass needle points under normal conditions. Then you could add a magnetic field and look at the change in the behavior of the needle. Identifying cause-and-effect relationships allows you to make predictions about related situations. You could predict that a compass needle will always point north because Earth's magnetic field prompts the needle to point in a consistent direction.

Does the introduction of wolves cause elk populations to decrease? Biologists might measure the size of the elk population before and after wolves settled in an area. While cause-and-effect relationships may seem obvious, they are not always true. For example, climate change could have resulted in the loss of nutrient rich grasses for elk to eat, leading to a decrease in the elk population.

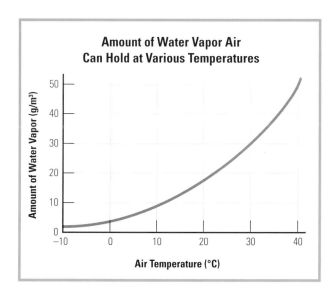

Amount of Water Vapor Air Can Hold at Various Temperatures

Does an increase in temperature indoors cause humidity to rise? First, you could measure the current humidity in a room. Then you could increase the air temperature of the room and measure if there was a change in humidity. It is important to only change the air temperature so there is only one cause to observe the effects of.

Scale, Proportion, and Quantity

Systems occur at different measures of size, time, and energy. Part of science is recognizing that different objects and situations occur at different scales, in different proportions, and in different amounts. Something that can be observed at one scale may not be observable at another scale. How can scale, proportion, and quantity help you understand phenomena in science?

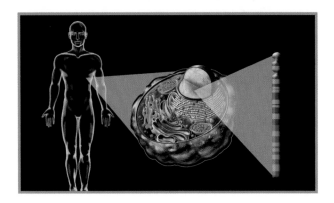

How can you describe the functions of the human body at different scales? Your whole body functions to eat, breathe, and move. At a smaller scale, cells, which can only be seen with a microscope, are the building parts for tissues and organs. Inside these cells is a nucleus, which contains chromosomes on an even smaller scale. Chromosomes are structures that contain instructions for how your body should grow.

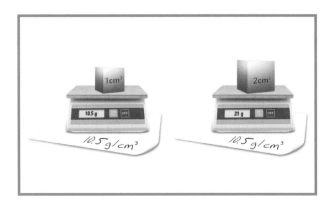

How can proportions be used to identify materials? Density is a proportion that can be used to identify materials. Here, there are two different cubes on a scale. The mass of each cube is different, just as the volume of each cube is different. However, the density of the two cubes is the same. Though the cubes are a different mass and volume, their density allows you to identify them as the same material.

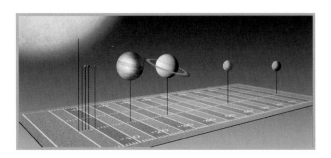

Why are different measurement units used to measure quantities in space? Within the solar system, scientists use astronomical units (AU) in which 1 AU is the average distance between the sun and Earth. However, the distances between stars are so far apart that scientists use a different unit of measurement—light years.

Systems and System Models

Systems occur in the natural world and in objects that are engineered by humans. Many systems interact with other ones, are parts of a larger complex one, or have subsystems of their own. How can you use the concept of systems to understand different phenomena such as the human body, a motor, and the motion of planets in the solar system?

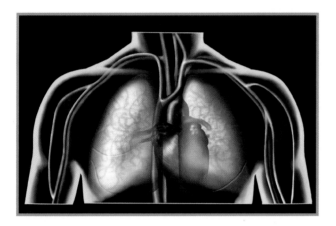

How do subsystems interact within the human body? Your whole body is composed of subsystems that work together to allow you to function. As your respiratory system draws in oxygen through your lungs, it sends oxygen to your bloodstream that is then carried through your body by the circulatory system. Both of these systems work together to help fulfill the body's needs. This is an example of two naturally occurring subsystems interacting as part of a complex whole.

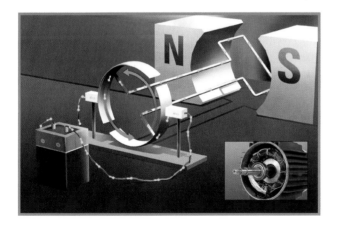

How does a model of a motor represent the way energy and matter flow through a system? This model of an electric motor shows that there is an energy input into the system from the battery. The energy is transferred to electrically charged particles in the motor's wires. The particles begin to flow, forming an electric current that flows past a magnet. The forces between the wires and the magnet cause the motor's shaft to spin, outputting energy.

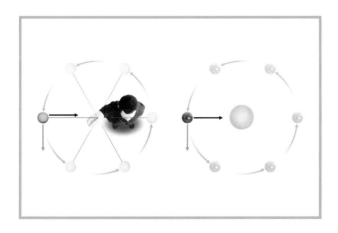

How can you use a model to represent the Earth-sun system? Suppose you swing a ball tied to a string around your head, causing it to move in a circle around your head. The string exerts a force on the ball, but the ball is moving fast enough to keep it from falling back into your hand. In this model, the string represents the gravitational force between the sun and Earth. Using a model allows you to understand how gravitational force functions in the Earth-sun system.

Energy and Matter

Systems can be described in term of energy and matter. Matter is anything that has mass and volume. Energy is the ability to cause motion or change. Energy takes two forms—kinetic energy, which is energy due to motion, and potential energy, which is stored energy. If you can track the energy in a system, you can use it to explain or predict motion and other changes. How does the transfer of energy drive motion or changes in each of the following systems?

How does a food web describe the transfer of energy and matter in an ecosystem? Energy can come from different places and is introduced into the food web when producers, such as plants, absorb energy from sunlight. Other organisms, called consumers, eat producers and other consumers to obtain their energy. Organisms use the energy they obtain to do things like move and stay warm. When they use this energy, they transfer energy to the environment.

Matter follows a path similar to energy in the food web. A consumer will eat an organism lower in the food web, consuming that organism's matter. However, unlike other organisms in the food web, producers get their matter from a different place than where they get their energy. Producers get matter from air, soil, and water, rather than sunlight. The matter from the air, soil, and water comes from decomposers that get their matter from the dead matter and wastes left behind by other organisms in the food web.

Matter and energy follow similar, but different paths. Matter is constantly being cycled through the ecosystem, while energy will flow in one direction.

How does a snowboarder transform potential energy into kinetic energy? Suppose a snowboarder was at the top of a hill, waiting to glide down to the bottom. A chairlift used energy from electricity to lift her up the mountain. That energy is stored by the snowboarder as potential energy. Since the mountain is so tall, she has a large amount of potential energy stored up.

Once the snowboarder tips over the ledge and glides down the hill, her potential energy begins to transform into kinetic energy. Kinetic energy is the energy an object has due to its motion. As the snowboarder is moving down the hill, not only is she moving herself, she is also moving the snow beneath her board. So, she is transferring some of her energy to the snow, giving it kinetic energy.

After the snowboarder glides to the bottom of the hill, nearly all of her potential energy has become kinetic energy. In order to stop, she must transfer all of her kinetic energy to her surroundings. Her board slides across the snow, spraying some of the snow forward and heating it up.

How does the transfer of energy drive the motion of matter in the water cycle?
Water particles are always moving, so they always have some kinetic energy. Water particles near the surface of water with a lot of kinetic energy evaporate off of the surface. When they do, they carry energy away from the water.

Since the particles that escaped the surface of the water have a lot of kinetic energy, they also have a high temperature. Their high temperature causes them to rise into the atmosphere. As they rise, their kinetic energy is converted into potential energy. Since the particles are losing kinetic energy, they also cool.

High in the atmosphere, slow-moving particles condense to form water droplets and clouds. These droplets are held high in the atmosphere due to updrafts of air.

During the precipitation stage, the water particles become too heavy to be held in the atmosphere by updrafts. They begin to fall, and their potential energy is converted back into kinetic energy. Even after reaching the ground, they continue to convert potential energy into kinetic energy as water flows down rivers and into the ocean.

Structure and Function

The structure and properties of a natural or engineered material often determine how that material will function. If a scientist or engineer can understand the structure of that material, then they can also determine how it should function and what may cause it to function improperly. How can you use the concept of structure and function to understand the behavior of natural and engineered materials?

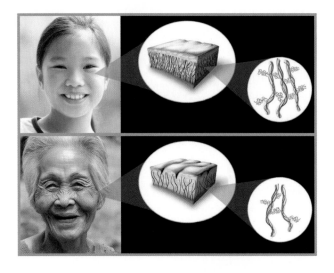

How do changes in the structure of skin tissue affect its function? Two of the proteins made by skin cells, collagen and elastin, help determine the skin's traits. When you are young, your skin continually replaces its collagen and elastin, which keeps your skin strong but flexible. Young skin is very good at protecting the underlying tissues of the body. Over time your body produces less of these proteins, resulting in more wrinkles and reduced protection, strength, and flexibility. The skin's functioning is directly related to the structural components that make it up.

How does the molecular structure of plastic affect its function? Plastics, such as the ones that make up water bottles, are polymers that are made of long flexible chains of molecules. Their structure allows them to retain their shape while remaining flexible. Biodegradable plastics are made of polymers that easily break down into smaller molecules over time. This allows the plastics to break down when buried in a landfill.

How do engineers use the properties of light and glass to design camera lenses? The structure and shape of the glass lens determines how well it functions as a medium for light waves. Glass can be shaped to refract the right amount of light, minimize absorption and reflection, and transmit light to the camera sensor. Once the structure is designed to be just right, the camera can get the perfect shot.

Stability and Change

Scientists can measure the behavior of systems by their stability, or resistance to change, and how they respond to change. Systems, whether small or large, will respond to any amount of change in different ways. How can you observe the way that systems respond when different amounts of change are introduced on different scales?

How can an ecosystem adjust to a change and reestablish its stability? When beavers construct a dam on a stream, they cause changes in the nonliving parts of the ecosystem. These changes in the nonliving parts of the ecosystem do not destroy the system but instead change which species can live there. The ecosystem adapts to changes over long time scales so that it is not completely disrupted. The ecosystem is able to reach a new state of stability.

How do stability and changes in your motion affect you when you ride in a car? If you are moving, you will continue moving at the same speed and in the same direction unless unbalanced forces are acting on you. In a car crash, this stable motion can be very dangerous. Unbalanced forces on the car cause the car to stop suddenly. If you are not wearing a seatbelt, there is no force pushing you back, so your motion will remain stable. You will keep moving forward.

How do different amounts of change over time effect the stability of Earth system? The amount of carbon dioxide in Earth's atmosphere took millions of years to slowly reach a level that supports animal life on land. But starting about 150 years ago, people have been adding large amounts of carbon dioxide in the air. This fast change caused many destabilizing effects to Earth's system, which causes changes in stability to subsystems such as weather and climate systems.

Analyzing Text Structure

After watching a television program about space, you decide to do some reading about our solar system. You have already found a long online article and a couple of books at the library, but there is a lot of information to read through. How can you get the most out of your reading in the least amount of time?

Identifying the Purpose of the Text One way to make sense of a text is to identify the author's purpose. An author may be writing for many different purposes, including any one of these three:

- **Persuasive Argument** The author tries to convince the reader that his or her argument is correct.

- **Tell a Story** The author informs the reader about a process or explains why something came to be.

- **Explanation of Facts** The author informs or teaches the reader about a subject or topic.

Identifying Text Structures Another way to analyze text is to figure out how the information is organized, or structured. Authors may use many different text structures, including the following:

- **Cause and Effect Structure** The author attempts to answer a question about what causes something to happen.

- **Chronological Structure** The author explains a series of events in order.

- **Compare and Contrast Structure** The author compares two or more subjects to argue or clarify facts.

Identifying Organizing Elements Look for specific features of the text that you can use to preview or review the text. A piece of text may have one or more of these organizing elements.

- **Table of Contents** The table of contents helps you identify where information is located in certain lessons or sections.

- **Introductions and Summaries** An introduction can provide previews of the text and explain the structure, while a summary can provide main ideas and a conclusion statement.

- **Headings** Reading headings provides information about the topic of a particular section of text.

- **Graphic Organizers** Visual aids organize large amounts of data into charts and graphs that are easy to understand.

Reading scientific texts can seem like a difficult task, but when you identify the structure and organization of the text, it becomes much easier to understand the topic you are reading about.

Common Roots, Prefixes, and Suffixes in Science

While reading, you come across the word *exoskeleton*. You know what *skeleton* means, but you wonder what *exo-* means. Knowing common roots, prefixes, and suffixes, and how they combine, can make unfamiliar science words easier to understand! Here is a list of some of the common roots, prefixes, and suffixes you may encounter when you are reading science related texts:

Root, Prefix, or Suffix	Meaning	Examples
astro-	pertaining to stars or celestial bodies	astronaut, astrophysics
bio-	life	biofuel, biomass, biome, biosphere
chem-, chemo-	chemical	chemical, chemistry, chemotherapy
eco-	environment, nature	ecology, ecosystem
endo-	within, inside	endoskeleton, endothermic
exo-	without, outside	exoskeleton, exothermic
gene-	pertaining to heredity	genes, genetics, mutagen
geo-	the earth, pertaining to Earth	geography, geology, geosphere
hyper-	over, above	hyperthermia
hypo-	under, below	hypothermia, hypodermic
macro-	very large in scale, scope, or capability	macroscopic
micro-	extremely small	microscope, microscopic
-ology	a science or branch of knowledge, the study of something	archaeology, biology, geology
poly-	many, several, more than one	polymer
-sphere	spherical shape, supporting life	atmosphere, biosphere, hydrosphere
therm-, thermo-	heat, hot	hypothermia, thermodynamics, thermometer

If you can recognize a common root, prefix, or suffix, you can identify the meaning of unfamiliar words. Insects commonly have exoskeletons. The prefix *exo-* means "without" or "outside."

Writing Scientific Arguments and Explanations

After making observations and conducting an experiment, your teacher gives you an assignment to write a scientific argument about your experiment. It may sound simple, but where do you start?

Scientists do a lot of hands-on experimentation, but they also write arguments that convince people their claims are true. Writing is very important to the scientific process—well-written observations and notes will help you write a strong argument.

Claim The claim is where you introduce your hypothesis or the answer to a question you are trying to solve by gathering data. This is also where you would establish a formal style. You can do this by using full sentences and scientific terms you may have learned in class.

Evidence Your evidence is specific scientific data that supports your claim. You can also use charts and graphs to communicate your findings. They make it easy to see and compare evidence, which can make your argument stronger.

When writing scientific arguments, it is useful to organize your data into charts or graphs and ask a peer to review your work. Doing these simple things will help to make your argument stronger and more convincing.

Reasoning After providing your evidence, you need to convince the reader that the evidence supports the claim. If your classmates have different claims, you can point these out and use evidence to tell the reader why your claim is correct. You may also write a concluding statement to refresh the reader's memory and summarize the evidence and related reasoning.

Before you finish writing a scientific argument, read it for any spelling and grammatical errors. It also helps to have a peer read your argument. If your peer does not understand your argument, you may need to rewrite it until how you came to your conclusion is clearer.

Writing Investigation Procedures

The steps needed to carry out an investigation are called a procedure. Scientists write a procedure as part of the process of designing an investigation and use the procedure as a guide during the investigation. Scientists also record a procedure so that their fellow scientists can follow the investigation easily and confirm results. How can you write a good investigation procedure?

A good procedure organizes steps and data easily so you can complete your experiment without running into problems or danger. A procedure should also be written so anybody can repeat your experiment and obtain an identical result. Use this checklist as a guide when writing your procedure and to evaluate your writing when you are done:

☑ All of the necessary steps are included and clearly labeled.

☑ The tools and materials for each step are listed.

☑ Each step is clearly written using precise language and vocabulary so that a classmate or any stranger can follow it.

☑ The steps are in the correct order.

☑ Safety notes are included for any steps that require them.

☑ The type of data you will collect in each step is clearly described.

☑ If necessary, a data table is prepared to record data in.

☑ The language of the procedure is unbiased and something a fellow scientist would be comfortable reading.

Once your teacher has reviewed your procedure, you are ready to conduct your investigation!

When writing an investigation procedure, it is important that the steps are clearly written, are in the right order, include the materials needed, and have identified safety precautions.

Communicating with Graphic Organizers

Your teacher divides the class into teams and gives you all an assignment to build a protective structure for an egg out of simple materials. Afterwards, you work together as a class to create a graphic organizer to explain all the information and see why different teams got different results.

Scientists use graphic organizers to visually communicate complex ideas or large amounts of data. If you can read a graphic organizer, you can explain the results you see. When gathering data, it is useful to take the information you have and sketch a graphic organizer by hand. Once you decide how to present the information on paper, you can create your graphic organizer on the computer. Many software programs have the tools you need to create graphic organizers, like flow charts, Venn diagrams, and tables.

Flow Chart Flow charts are useful for displaying processes. In this case, the flowchart is explaining the process your team used to build your egg protector. You can add more detailed information to each box, but the chart should be a step-by-step explanation of each stage of your work. Computers have many applications that can be used to create flowcharts, including word processors or paint applications. The flowchart you see here is a good reference for the process you should follow when designing a solution to a problem.

Defining the Engineering Problem
- Clearly state the problem to be solved
- Define criteria for egg container
- Define constraints of egg container

Optimizing the Design Solution
- Optimize design of egg container
- Retest egg container
- Optimize container more if needed

Developing Possible Solutions
- Develop egg container designs
- Narrow down egg container designs
- Design egg container
- Test egg container

Tables Tables group information into various categories by columns and rows and are useful for displaying large amounts of data. Scientists use tables to help them observe patterns in their data. In this case, the table displays the different materials used by the teams in your class to create their egg protectors. You can create a table by using spreadsheet software and inputting information into cells or by hand-drawing rows and columns on a sheet of paper. Look at the table below. Can you see any patterns in the materials used by the teams to create their egg protectors?

Team 1	Team 2	Team 3
Tissue Paper	Tissue Paper	Tissue Paper
Wooden sticks	Cotton Balls	Paper cup
Tape	Plastic Bag	Tape

Venn Diagram Like flowcharts, computers have applications that can be used to create Venn diagrams. Venn diagrams are used to show similarities and differences; each circle lists the traits of an object, and the overlap is used to list similarities. They are useful when comparing the traits of two or three different objects or ideas. Consider the Venn diagram below. Which material was used by all teams? Which materials were only used by one team? What conclusions would you be able to draw from this based on the results of the experiment?

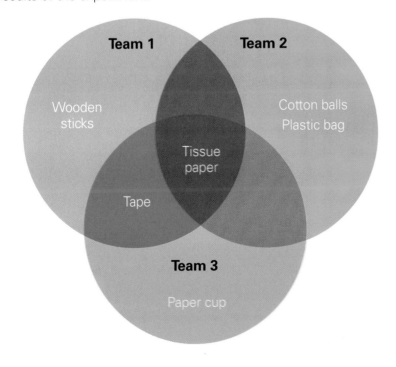

Research Project Tips

After reading about the periodic table, you decide you want to research it as a research project topic for your science class. One of the first things you need to do is find sources. With so many different places to look, including online and print sources, how do you even know where to begin?

How to Find Sources

- **First, go to the library.** The reference librarian will be able to point you in the right direction and teach you how to use the online catalog to find books, magazines, and journal subscriptions.

- **Find reliable sources.** Government and university websites, scientific magazines and journals, and other major magazines can be valuable sources of information that are easy to access.

- **Start general with search engines.** When using search engines, use words you would expect to find in your source. You do not need to worry about capitalization. Most search engines are able to understand what you are trying to find.

- **Try an advanced search tool.** Many search engines have a button for an "advanced search." Here, you can tell the search engine which kinds of websites you are looking for. If you want to find a government website, you can type "site:.gov" into one of the search fields.

The library is one of your best resources for research. Not only does it have books, it also has subscriptions for online magazines and journals that have current information on scientific advancements.

How to Evaluate Sources

- **Evaluate whether a source has bias.** Consider whether the source has arguments that are either supported by widely accepted facts or available data. If you find information on a website that is very different from some of your other sources, you may want to reconsider using that source.

- **Evaluate the source of your source.** Unofficial websites that are not supported by scientific, government, or academic institutions are probably not good sources to use. Check the URL for clues. Websites that end in .gov or .edu tend to be more reliable than general .com sites. You can also read a source's "About" page to see what their intention is for the information they provide.

- **Evaluate the quality of your source.** One source that has a lot of information about one topic can be more useful than several sources that have a little information about one topic.

How to Cite Sources

- **Keep track of which sources you use.** Keep notes as to which sources you use and where you use them in your own work. It helps to use bookmarks that you can label to mark which pages you draw information from. Another easy way to keep track of your sources is to make a copy of the first page of a book or article, or take a screenshot of a webpage. You may also want to create a spreadsheet or document that keeps track of the name of a source, its title or URL, and the information you took from the site.

- **Use a style manual.** There are several guides that teach you how to cite sources. The APA Style Manual, MLA Handbook, and Chicago Manual of Style are good places to start.

- **Avoid plagiarism.** When you quote a source or use information you got from a source, you need to give the source credit. The style manuals will have instructions on how to give credit for different kinds of sources.

As you gather information from sources, it is very important to keep track of which sources you use. Keep organized notes for online sources by creating a document or spreadsheet. Label paper bookmarks or sticky notes for print sources.

Positive and Negative Numbers

Positive and negative numbers are used together to describe quantities having opposite directions or values. Positive numbers represent values greater than zero, while negative numbers represent values less than zero. How can you use positive and negative numbers to describe changes in temperature?

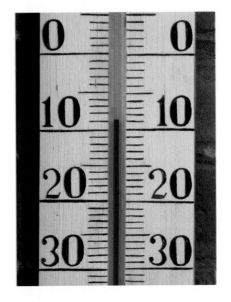

Thermometers display temperatures on a vertical number line. Numbers below zero on the number line are negative temperatures, while numbers above zero are positive temperatures.

A weather report says the temperature is –5°C. A negative number is a number that is less than zero. A number line represents numbers in relation to zero. On a horizontal number line, negative numbers are to the left of zero and positive numbers are to the right of zero. So, –5°C is five degrees below zero, which is five degrees to the left of zero. Likewise, 5°C would be five degrees above zero which is 5 degrees to the right of zero on a number line diagram.

During the afternoon, the temperature rises. The weather report says that the temperature increased by 7°C. What is the temperature now? To add a positive number, move right along the number line.

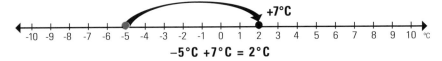

$$-5°C + 7°C = 2°C$$

After sunset, the temperature drops, or decreases in value. The weather report says the temperature dropped 10°C after sunset. What is the temperature now? When you subtract a positive number, you move left along the number line.

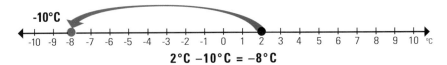

$$2°C - 10°C = -8°C$$

What is the difference between the temperature in the morning (–5°C) and the temperature after sunset (–8°C)? To find the difference, subtract the morning temperature from the current temperature. To subtract a negative number means to add the positive of that number, so move right on the number line, just like adding a positive number.

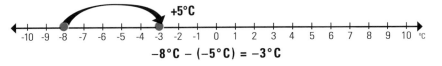

$$-8°C - (-5°C) = -3°C$$

Exponents and Scientific Notation

Scientists often need to represent very small numbers and very large numbers, which have many digits. These numbers can be so long that they are difficult to read. So, scientists developed a simpler method to represent these numbers, called scientific notation.

Scientific notation requires the use of exponents. An exponent is a number or symbol indicating how many times a base number should be multiplied by itself. For example, the "5" in 8^5 is an exponent, and 8^5 can also be expressed as "eight to the power of five" or $8 \times 8 \times 8 \times 8 \times 8$.

When you write numbers using scientific notation, 10 is the always the base number. Each time you multiply by 10, you move the decimal point one place to the right. So, multiplying by 10^6 moves the decimal point six places to the right. Scientific notation takes a number between 0 and 10 and multiplies it by a power of 10. This calculation moves the decimal point to the left or right the correct number of places.

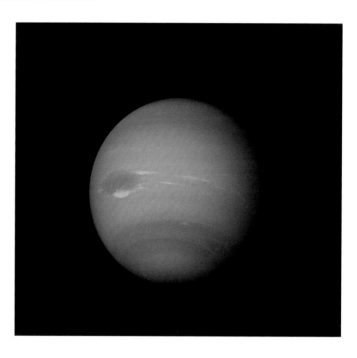

Scientists use scientific notation to represent very small and very large numbers using powers of 10. Neptune is approximately 4,700,000,000 km from Earth, which can be written in scientific notation as 4.7×10^9 km.

Scientific notation is useful for writing very large numbers that represent distances in space. For example, engineers designing a probe to send to Neptune would often need to refer to the distance between Earth and Neptune, which is 4,700,000,000.0 kilometers. 4,700,000,000.0 can be expressed as 4.7 with the decimal point moved to the right nine places.

$$4.7 \times 10^9 \text{ km} = 4,700,000,000.0 \text{ km}$$

Very small numbers can also be written using scientific notation. For example, the diameter of a hydrogen atom is approximately 0.000000000106 meters. To write small numbers, you divide by 10 instead of multiplying by 10. You can represent this in scientific notation using negative exponents. 0.000000000106 meters is 1.06 meters with the decimal point moved to the left 10 times.

$$1.06 \times 10^{-10} \text{ m} = 0.0000000000106 \text{ m}$$

Dependent and Independent Variables

Scientists use dependent and independent variables to describe the relationships they measure in their investigations. Independent and dependent variables are used in equations to represent two different quantities that change in relationship to one another.

A commercial airplane has a cruising air speed for long-distance flights of 900 km/hr. In this relationship, the distance the plane travels depends on how long the plane has been flying. However, the time it has been flying does not depend on the distance it has traveled. So, time is the independent variable (x), and distance is the dependent variable (y). The relationship between kilometers traveled and the time in hours can be represented between two variables using an equation, a table, or a graph.

An equation that represents the relationship between the distance the airplane has traveled and how long it has traveled is:

$$y = 900x$$

The letter x represents the independent variable, which is the time the plane has been flying. The letter y is the dependent variable, which is the distance the plane has traveled.

The second way to represent the relationship between variables is with a table. The table on this page uses the equation $y = 900x$ to calculate the dependent y value that matches each independent x value in the table. It represents the relationship between x and y.

The third way to represent the relationship between two variables is with a graph. You can use either the equation or the table of values to represent the relationship in a graph. The graph both shows the equation and plots the points from the data table.

Equations, tables, and graphs are three ways to represent the relationship between an independent variable x and a dependent variable y. For a plane flying at 900 km/hr, the independent variable is flying time, and the dependent variable is distance traveled.

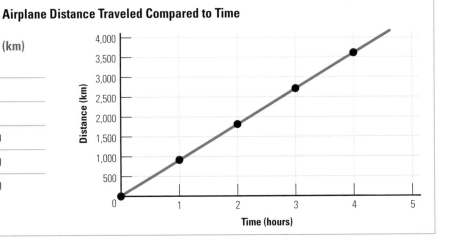

Airplane Distance Traveled Compared to Time

Time (hours) x	Distance (km) y
0	0
1	900
2	1,800
3	2,700
4	3,600

Chance and Probability

Some events scientists study involve things that definitely will happen or will not happen. However, most events might happen but will not happen for sure. How can understanding probability help predict how likely events are to happen?

Every year, sugar maple trees produce many seeds, which are carried away from the trees by wind. Many of the seeds germinate, or sprout into a seedling that can grow into a new tree, but not every seed does. A scientist decides to study how likely it is that a maple seed will sprout. That is, she will study the probability that a seed will germinate.

The scientist randomly collects a sample of 1,000 seeds from trees in a 1 km × 1 km area. She and her team plant the seeds in a large field. They return in the spring to determine how many of the seeds germinated into new maple trees. She might find that 910 of the seeds germinated. The proportion of seeds that germinated was $\frac{910}{1,000}$, or 91%.

Her team repeats the experiment several more times in different years and finds that in one year, 97% of the seeds germinated. In the second year, 94% germinated, and 95% germinated in the third year. From this data, she finds the average proportion of seeds that germinate and concludes that the chance of a maple seed germinating is about 95%.

Sugar maple trees produce many seeds, but some seeds do not germinate. By collecting data on how many seeds germinate, a scientist can estimate the probability that each individual seed will germinate.

A 95% probability means that each seed has a 95 in 100 chance of germinating. If you looked at 100 seeds, you would expect 95 of them to germinate. If you looked at 1,000 seeds, you would expect 950 to germinate. However, 950 seeds would not germinate every time. For example, sometimes 962 seeds would germinate, or 935 seeds, or 900 seeds, or even all 1,000 seeds. A probability describes the chance that something will happen, but it does not predict exactly what will happen every time.

Representing and Interpreting Data

Scientific investigations produce a lot of data, but it is often difficult to make sense of the data the way it is recorded during the investigation. Scientists carefully choose how they will represent data to make it easy to analyze, interpret, and communicate its meaning to others.

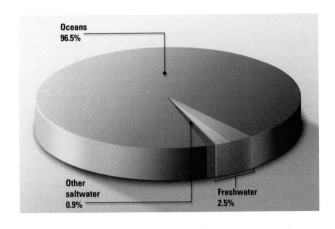

Pie Graphs A comparison between the amount of freshwater and saltwater on Earth is best represented using a pie graph. Scientists use pie graphs to display data with percentages. A pie graph, also known as a pie chart, divides a circle into sections to show the relative sizes of data and how a part relates to the whole. A pie graph can effectively show how one variable is divided between different categories. They often show the percentage of a variable in each category. For instance, the wedges on this pie graph show how the water on Earth is divided into three categories: water from oceans, fresh water, and other saltwater.

Scatter Plots Scientists use scatter plots to show repeated measurements of a similar phenomenon, such as the relationship between the waiting time between eruptions of the geyser Old Faithful and the length of the eruptions. Each measurement of an eruption is one point on the graph. The x coordinate of the point shows the duration of the eruption. The y coordinate shows the waiting time before the eruption. Scatter plots are effective for comparing two variables that do not fall into specific categories. There are many patterns in data that scatter plots can reveal.

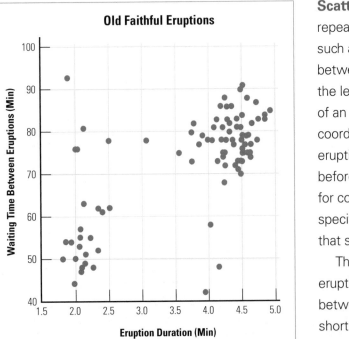

The scatter plot shows that Old Faithful eruptions fall into two main groups: a short wait between eruptions (45–60 minutes) followed by a short eruption (2 minutes), or a long wait between eruptions (70–90 minutes) followed by a long eruption (4–5 minutes).

A scatter plot that compares shoe size to height would probably form a line, indicating that people who are taller usually wear larger shoes.

Bar Graphs This bar graph of earthquakes in Oklahoma shows how many earthquakes occurred in Oklahoma in each year between 2000 and 2015. Scientists use bar graphs, or bar charts, to represent the relative sizes of data values in different categories, such as years, months, colors, or cities. They use horizontal or vertical bars to represent the size of the value in each category. Larger bars represent a higher value, and smaller bars represent a lower value. The bar graph of earthquakes in Oklahoma shows a huge increase in earthquakes in 2014 from previous years since the bar for 2014 is much larger than any of the previous bars.

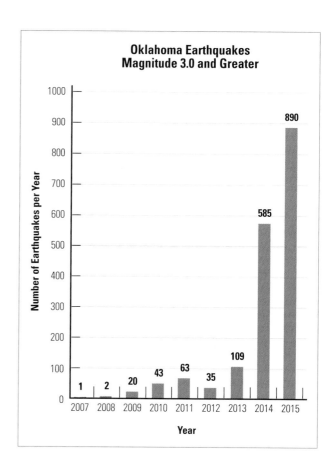

Line Graphs Scientists use line graphs to show how a dependent variable changes as an independent variable is increased. In many cases, the independent variable is a measure of time, so the graph shows how a dependent variable changes over time. For example, the average global temperature over time can be shown using a line graph. Like in a scatter plot, each data point has an x coordinate (time) and a y coordinate (average temperature). Unlike a scatter plot, each data point is connected to the last one with a straight line. Following the line shows how the average temperature changed over time.

This line graph shows many patterns about how the global average temperature changed between 1880 and 2000. The temperature was lowest between 1900 and 1920 and highest after 2000. What other patterns do you see in the graph?

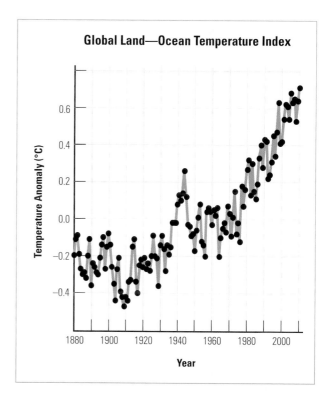

Ratios, Rates, Percents, and Proportional Relationships

When scientists collect data involving numbers, quantities are often compared. You can compare quantities using ratios, percentages, and unit rates. How are these mathematical concepts useful in understanding one of the most important scientific investigations related to changes in species?

Scientists have been observing and studying dark peppered moths near Manchester, England, since 1848. More than 70 species of moths in England have undergone a change from light to dark, with similar observations in the United States.

Kettlewell released light and dark colored moths and then recaptured them to study how well each type of moth survived in polluted and unpolluted woods. He used the ratio of moths captured to moths released, expressed as a percentage, to support his findings.

Expressing Ratios as Percentages To study this change, a scientist named Henry Bernard Davis Kettlewell released light and dark colored moths in polluted and unpolluted woods. He then recaptured as many of the moths as he could over the next week. In the unpolluted woods, he released 496 light colored moths and captured back 62 of them. So, the ratio of captured moths to released moths is 62:496. By finding an equivalent ratio with 100 as the number of moths released, you can find what percentage 62:496 equals.

$$62:496 = 12.5:100$$

Kettlewell recaptured 12.5% of the light moths he released. Similarly, he released 488 dark moths into the unpolluted woods and only recaptured 34. That is 34:488 as a ratio, or 7.0% as a percentage.

Using Unit Rates Scientists often compare quantities using unit rates. A unit rate is the number of one quantity there is for every one unit of another quantity. If Kettlewell wanted to know how many moths he needed to release in order to capture one moth, he would calculate the unit rate. He would do so by starting with the ratio of moths released to moths captured (496:62 for light colored moths). Then he would find an equivalent ratio where the number of moths captured is one. Unit rates are usually written as fractions.

$$\text{Unit rate} = \frac{8 \ \textit{moths released}}{1 \ \textit{moth captured}}$$

So, for every eight light colored moths Kettlewell released, he captured one light colored moth back.

Graphing and Interpreting Proportional Relationships

Scientists and engineers look for proportional relationships to better understand and predict how two variables are related. In a proportional relationship, the ratio of one variable to the other is always the same. How can using proportional reasoning make someone a better bowler?

An engineer wants to improve her bowling score, so she decides to study the relationship between the mass of the bowling ball she uses and the kinetic energy of the ball. She builds a machine that throws a bowling ball down the lane at exactly 8 m/s. Then she tests a variety of bowling balls. She makes a table of her data and finds the ratio of energy to mass of the balls. She sees that the ratio is the same for every ball moving at 8 m/s. She discovered a proportional relationship between the bowling ball's energy and mass.

She makes a graph of the data in her table and sees that the data points form a straight line. The line passes through the origin (0, 0). She calculates that the slope of the line is 32 J/kg. The line's slope is the same as the ratio of energy per unit mass in her table.

To make predictions, the engineer writes an equation to describe her data. The equation of a straight line is $y = mx + b$. The y-intercept (b) of her line is 0 J. The slope (m) of her line is 32 J/kg. So, the equation for her line is:

$$y = 32x$$

In this equation, y is energy of the ball, and x is mass of the ball. The engineer now knows how the energy of the ball depends on its mass. But she still has more questions. How does the energy depend on the speed of the ball? And how much energy should the ball have to knock down all the pins?

Mass versus Kinetic Energy With Constant Velocity

Mass (kg)	Energy (J)	Ratio: energy/ mass (J/kg)
4	128	$\frac{128}{4} = 32$
5	160	$\frac{160}{5} = 32$
6	192	$\frac{192}{6} = 32$
7	224	$\frac{224}{7} = 32$

Angles, Perpendicular and Parallel Lines

Scientists use angles as well as parallel and perpendicular lines to describe how objects are oriented relative to each other. How can using these mathematical ideas help when explaining how light rays interact with a glass slide?

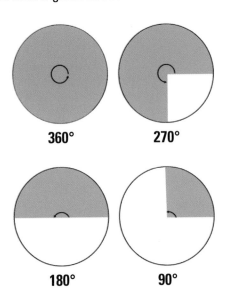

360°   270°

180°   90°

Angles Light travels in a straight line until it passes from one material, or medium, to another material. When a beam of light enters a glass slide, it bends. The amount that the beam bends depends on the angle between the slide and the beam of light. An angle is a shape formed by two rays that begin at the same endpoint, and the size of the angle can be changed by rotating the two rays. Angles are measured in degrees (°). Rotating 360° is rotating in a full circle, returning the object back to where it started. Rotating by 180° is rotating through half a circle, and rotating by 90° is rotating a quarter circle.

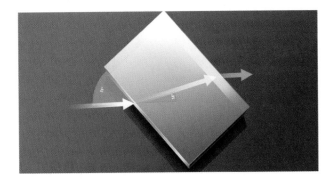

Parallel Lines The beam of light meets the glass at a 51° angle. As it enters the glass, it changes direction, turning 14° counterclockwise. When the beam of light leaves the glass, it rotates back, turning 14° clockwise. The beam of light leaving the glass is parallel to the beam of light entering the glass. Parallel lines are lines that, if you extend them out infinitely in both directions, will never cross.

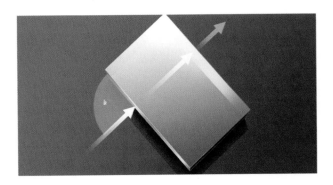

Perpendicular Lines A beam of light will not always bend when it enters a glass slide. If the beam of light is perpendicular to the edge of the slide, the light will pass straight through without bending. Two lines are perpendicular if they meet at a 90° angle.

Area, Surface Area, and Volume

Scientists use area, surface area, and volume to describe the sizes of various objects they study. Area describes the size of a two-dimensional surface. Surface area describes the total size of the surface of a three-dimensional object. Volume describes the amount of space a three-dimensional object takes up. How could a scientist who wanted to explain why cells are so small use the concepts of area, surface area, and volume? He investigates simple cube-shaped cells in the human body.

Area The scientist knows that for a cell to survive, enough nutrients have to pass through its cell membrane to supply the needs of the cell. The larger the area of the membrane, the more nutrients can pass through it. So, the scientist calculates the area of one square-shaped side of the cell.

$$Area = s^2$$

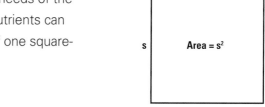

Surface Area But the scientist knows that nutrients can pass through any side of the cube, not just one side. So, he needs to calculate the surface area of the cube. The surface area is the total area of the surface of the cube. The cube has six sides, so its surface area is six times the area of one side.

$$Surface\ Area = 6s^2$$

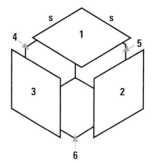

Volume However, the scientist knows that volume of the cube is important too. The volume is the total amount of space that the cube takes up. Generally, the larger the volume is, the more nutrients the cell needs to stay alive and the farther the nutrients have to go after entering the cell. The volume of a cube is the side length cubed.

$$Volume = s^3$$

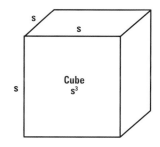

The scientist sees that as the cube gets larger, the volume grows much faster than the surface area grows. So, he decides that the cells he is studying are all very small because a large cell would not be able to take in enough nutrients through its membrane to support its volume. Cells need a large surface-area-to-volume ratio to survive.

Metric System Units

Throughout history, people around the world used different measurement units for trading goods and building objects and structures. Body parts were used to measure length. Grains of wheat were poured into containers to measure volume. Notches on a burning candle measured time. What problems did these customs cause, and how were they solved?

Traditional measurement units were awkward. It was difficult to compare one unit to another. Even when the same unit was used, there were often variations in how the unit was applied from place to place. In the late 1700s, that all changed. Scientists began to develop new units that were easy to use and accepted by scientists everywhere. Many of those units are part of the metric system.

The units you choose are determined by the goal of your investigation. If you want to measure the amount of matter in a rock, you would choose grams, a measure of mass, as your unit. If you want to measure how warm water is, you would use degrees Celsius. Other metric units are a combination of two units. For example, to describe the speed of a toy car rolling down a ramp, you would record the speed as meters per second.

Some Common Units of the Metric System

Measurement	Unit Name	Symbol
length	meter	m
mass	gram	g
time	second	s
temperature	degrees Celsius	°C
area	meter squared	m^2
frequency	hertz	Hz
force	newton	N
volume	meter cubed	m^3
density	kilogram per meter cubed	kg/m^3
speed, velocity	meter per second	m/s
acceleration	meter per second squared	m/s^2
energy	joule	J
power (energy per second)	watt	W
energy	watt hour	Wh
electric charge	coulomb	C

212   Learning Resources

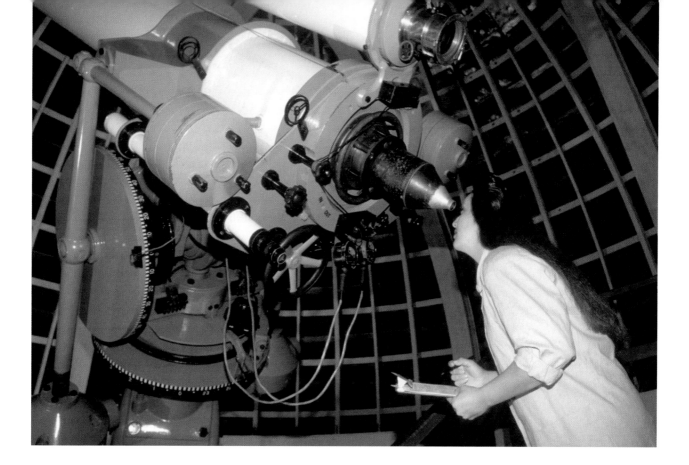

Some units were not developed as part of the metric system, but are still used by many scientists and engineers around the world. For example, if you want to compare distances of objects in the solar system, meters or even kilometers make the numbers difficult to communicate. Astronomers prefer to use astronomical units for this purpose. Similarly, when you need to describe distances between two stars or two galaxies, astronomical units are difficult. The distances are so great that astronomers use a unit called a light year, which is the distance that light travels in one Earth year.

Several measurement units are not part of the metric system, yet they are widely used by scientists and engineers. Two of these units, astronomical units and light years, are essential for communicating data to scientists such as this astronomer.

Some Common Units Outside the Metric System

Measurement	Unit Name	Symbol
time	minute	min
time	hour	h
time	day	d
angle size	degree	°
liquid volume	liter	L
distances inside the solar system	astronomical unit	AU
distances between stars	light year	ly
energy	calorie	cal
digital information	byte	B

Metric System Prefixes

A base unit can be modified using prefixes that indicate different amounts of each unit. Let's say you are investigating plant species to determine how much variation there is among their flower sizes. Some plant species have flowers that are so tiny that they can only be seen with magnification. Others have flowers as wide as a human's arm length. How can understanding measurement prefixes help you?

This flower is produced by plants called *Rafflesia* and is about 1 m across. Most plants have flowers that are much smaller, so smaller units are more useful for describing them.

Using prefixes with base units allows you to choose the unit that is simplest to communicate. Adding a prefix to a base unit makes a new unit. The new unit is made larger or smaller than the base unit by multiplying the base unit by a certain factor of 10. Each prefix represents a different factor of 10.

Here is how it works when measuring length. Meters are the base unit for length and are suitable for describing the size of the largest flowers in the plant kingdom. Millimeters have the prefix *milli*, which is 0.001. So a millimeter is 0.001, or 1/1,000, times the amount of one meter. There are 1,000 millimeters in one meter. Millimeters is a suitable unit for measuring the smallest flowers in the world. Now, suppose you were to travel around the world touring exotic flowers. A larger unit for length would be helpful to describe the distance you traveled. There are 1,000 meters in a kilometer. The prefix *kilo* means 10^3, or 1,000. So a kilometer is 1,000 times the size of a meter.

Many base units can be changed to easier-to-use units by adding a prefix. Start by choosing a base unit. Move up to get larger units and move down to get smaller units.

Some Common Units of the Metric System

Prefix	Symbol	Word	Decimal	Factor of 10
tera	T	trillion	1,000,000,000,000	10^{12}
giga	G	billion	1,000,000,000	10^9
mega	M	million	1,000,000	10^6
kilo	k	thousand	1,000	10^3
hecto	h	hundred	100	10^2
deka	da	ten	10	10^1
Choose a base unit.		one	1	10^0
deci	d	tenth	0.1	10^{-1}
centi	c	hundredth	0.01	10^{-2}
milli	m	thousandth	0.001	10^{-3}
micro	μ	millionth	0.000001	10^{-6}
nano	n	billionth	0.000000001	10^{-9}
pico	p	trillionth	0.000000000001	10^{-12}

Converting Measurement Units

You can also find equivalents of measurements that have the same base unit but different prefixes. One method is to divide or multiply by the number of one unit in the other unit. Another method is to use a metric "staircase" to decide how many places, and in what direction, to move the decimal point.

You can convert a larger unit to a smaller unit using multiplication. To do so, multiply the original measurement by the amount that the new unit differs from it. For example, to convert 9 kilometers to centimeters, you would multiply 9 (the number of kilometers) times 100,000 (the number of centimeters in one kilometer). So, 900,000 cm is equivalent to 9 km.

A smaller unit can be converted to a larger unit by using division. To do so, divide the original measurement by the amount that the new unit differs from it. For example, to use division to convert 900,000 centimeters to kilometers, divide 900,000 (the number of centimeters) by 100,000 (the number of centimeters in one kilometer). As before, 9 km is equivalent to 900,000 cm.

Another way to convert units is by picturing the metric "staircase" shown here to decide how many places to move the decimal point. For example, to convert 1.1 kilograms to milligrams, take six steps down the staircase and move the decimal point six places to the right. There are 1,100,000 milligrams in 1.1 kilograms.

In the United States, certain non-metric units are used in everyday situations. For this reason, you may sometimes need to convert non-metric units into metric units. Luckily, there are many websites and apps that will do conversions for you!

To convert to a larger unit, move the decimal point to the left for each step up the staircase. To convert to a smaller unit, move the decimal point to the right for each step you take down the staircase.

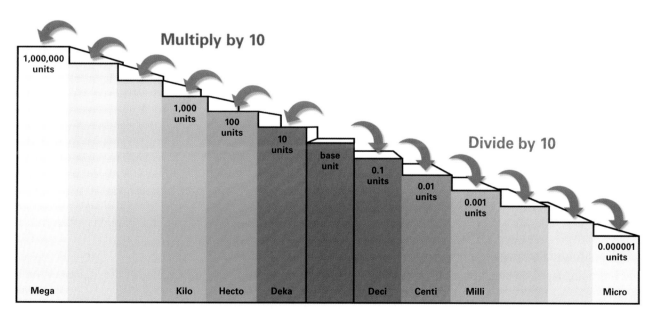

GLOSSARY

A

asteroid   a small rocky or metallic object that revolves around the sun

astronomical unit   a unit of measurement equal to the average distance between Earth and the sun; about 150 million km

axis   an imaginary line around which a rotating object turns

B

black hole   an object that is so dense that nothing within a certain distance from it can escape its gravitational field

C

celestial object   a natural object in space

circumpolar star   a star that is always above the horizon when viewed from a given latitude

comet   a small object made of rock, ice, and dust that has a highly elliptical orbit around the sun and gives off gas and dust in a tail as it travels close to the sun

constraint   a limitation on an engineering solution

criteria   the requirements that must be met for an engineering solution to be successful

D

data   information collected that can be used to support explanations

density   a physical property of matter that describes the amount of mass in a unit of volume

dwarf planet   a celestial object that directly revolves around the sun, has a nearly spherical shape, but has not cleared the neighborhood around its orbit

E

eclipse   an event in which the shadow of one celestial object falls on another celestial object

equinox   a time of year when the sun is directly overhead at the equator at noon, when day and night are of equal length

evidence   information that supports or refutes a theory

F

first quarter moon   the lunar phase where the moon, Earth, and the sun form a perpendicular angle; the moon looks like a semicircle with only the right half visible

full moon   the lunar phase where Earth is directly between the sun and the moon; the moon looks like a circle

G

galaxy   a collection of stars, dust, and gases held together by gravitational forces

gas planet   a planet that has a deep atmosphere and no rocky surface

gravitational force   an attractive force between all objects that have mass

ground-based telescope   a telescope that is placed on Earth's surface

L

light-year   a unit of length equal to the distance that light travels in space in one year

lunar eclipse   an eclipse that happens when the moon passes through Earth's shadow

lunar phase   the appearance of the lit area of the moon as seen from Earth

M

model   a representation which displays some but not all aspects of an object or phenomenon

moon   a celestial object that indirectly revolves around a star

N

nebula   a large cloud of gas and dust in space

new moon   the lunar phase where the moon is directly between Earth and the sun; the new moon cannot be seen from Earth

O

orbit   the path that an object follows as it revolves around another object

orbital plane   the plane in which an object's orbit lies

orbital radius   the average distance at which a planet revolves around the sun

P

penumbra   the lighter part of a shadow that surrounds the umbra

planet   an object that directly revolves around a star, has a nearly spherical shape, and has cleared the neighborhood around its orbit

planetary radius   the distance from the center of the planet's core to the outer edge of its atmosphere

R

revolution   the motion of an object around another object in space

rotation   the spin of an object around a point or line

S

scale   the level of measurement being used

scale model   a representation of a system that has the same relative sizes or distances as the actual system

scientific theory   a well-tested explanation of scientific observations and experiments

solar eclipse   an eclipse that happens when light from the sun is blocked by the moon, and the moon's shadow falls on Earth

solar system   a star and all the objects that travel around it

solstice   a time of year when the sun is directly overhead at one of the tropics during noon

space telescope   a telescope that is located in outer space

supernova   a gigantic explosion of a large star

system   a set of connected parts that form a complex whole

T

terrestrial planet   a planet that has a hard, rocky surface

third quarter moon   the lunar phase where the moon, Earth, and the sun form a perpendicular angle; the moon looks like a semicircle with only the left half visible

tropic   the latitudes furthest north and south that receive sunlight at a perpendicular angle

U

umbra   the darker, central part of a shadow

universe   all the space, time, matter, and energy that exists

INDEX

*Page numbers in **bold** indicate definitions.*

above Earth's orbital plane, 15
Alkaid, 147
circumpolar, 7, 15
locating, 16–17
measuring distances between, 146–147, 155
motion of, 7
near Earth's orbital plane, 15
patterns of, 12–13
Proxima Centauri, *see* Proxima Centauri (star)
Stonehenge, 33
structure
of cause and effect, 194
chronological structure, 194
compare and contrast, 194
and function, 192
of the Milky Way Galaxy, 149
patterns in, 134
of terrestrial planets, 92
text structure, 194
suffixes in science, 195
sun
apparent size of, 63
Earth-sun-moon system, *see* earth-sun-moon system
gravitational force of, 74, 75
orientation during a solar eclipse, 61
patterns of motion, 12–13
Proxima Centauri, distance to, 146
and the seasons, 30–32, 33
sunlight
angle of, 26–27
sunrise, 32
sun's energy
Earth's shape and, 25–26, 33
and the seasons, 30–31
sunset, 32
sun's path in sky
capturing, 34–37
pinhole camera, capturing with, 36–37
the seasons and, 32, 33
supernova, 133, **135**
surface area, 211
systems models, 189

system(s), 23, **27,** 189

T

tables, 199
telescopes
Arecibo Radio Telescope, 159
engineering design, 154–155
ground-based, 89, 90
Hale Telescope, 154-155
Hooker Telescope, 154
Hubble Space Telescope, *see* Hubble Space Telescope
radio, 157, 159
reflecting, **154**
refracting, **154**
space, 89, 91
WISE Telescope, 139
terrestrial planet(s), 89, **92**
atmosphere of, 92
center of, 92
formation of, 137
gravitational forces, 92, 93
key characteristics of, 92–94, 103
mass of, 92
orbital characteristics of, 92, 93
scale models of, 92, 112
structure of, 92
surface characteristics of, 92, 93
testability of questions, 166
text structure, 194
theory, *see* scientific theory
third quarter moon, 39, 43, **44,** 45
tides, 48
earth's revolution and, 51
earth's rotation and, 51
gravity and, 50
moon and, 50
timing of, 49
Titan (Saturn's moon), 117
total lunar eclipse, 57
total solar eclipse, 58
transfer of energy, 190–191
Tropic of Cancer, 28
Tropic of Capricorn, 28
tropics, 23, **28**
Trygg, Tarja (artist), 36, 37

twin Earths, 158
Tyson, Neil deGrasse (astrophysicist), 84–87

U

umbra, 53, **54**
Earth's umbra, *see* Earth's umbra
unit rates, 208
units of measurement, *see* measurement units
universe, 145, **152,** 155
scale of objects in, 153
Uranus, 118, 123
density of, 113, 118
gravitational forces of, 118
moons of, 118
orbital characteristics of, 118
outer solar system, model of, 121
rings of, 118
rotation of, 134, 137
viewing, 83

V

variable(s)
dependent, 204
independent, 204
Venn diagrams, 199
Venus, 89, 95, 103
gravitational force(s) of, 74, 93
mass of, 95
model of inner solar system, 101
orbital characteristics of, 95
radius of, 95
rotation of, 134, 137
surface characteristics of, 95, 96
viewing, 82
Venus Rover, 96–97, 103
volume, 211
Voyager 1, 109, 111, 122
Voyager 2, 111, 114, 118, 119

W

waning crescent moon, 43, 44
waning gibbous moon, 43, 44
waxing crescent moon, 43, 44
waxing gibbous moon, 43, 44

CREDITS

Front Matter
i: NASA/JPL-Caltech/MSSS iii: Getty Images xviiiT: iStockphoto xviiiB: Thinkstock xixT: iStockphoto xixB: iStockphoto xxiT: Shutterstock xxiC: Shutterstock xxiB: Shutterstock xxii: Thinkstock xxiii: Thinkstock xxiv: Getty Images xxv: Getty Images xxvi: iStockphoto xxvii: Getty Images xxixL: Getty Images xxixR: Hero Images Inc./Alamy xxx: iStockphoto xxxi: iStockphoto

Unit 1 Opener
2: All Canada Photos/Alamy 3T: Kwiktor/Dreamstime 3TC: Евгений Баранов/Dreamstime 3BC: Larry Landolfi/Science Source 3B: Fred Espenak/Science Source 5T: Ted Kinsman/Science Source 5L: Thinkstock 5R: NASA

Lesson 1
6: Kwiktor/Dreamstime 16: Lana Brooks/Dreamstime 16: Gpointstudio/Dreamstime 18: NASA/JPL-Caltech 19: NASA/JPL-Caltech/Space Science Institute 20: NASA/JPL/USGS 21: Thinkstock

Lesson 2
22: Евгений Баранов/Dreamstime 24T: ASSOCIATED PRESS 24B: ASSOCIATED PRESS 32: Ted Kinsman/Science Source 33: Laurence Delderfield/Alamy 34TR: Tarja Trygg 34BR: Tarja Trygg 34TL: Tarja Trygg 34BL: Tarja Trygg 35: Cealbiero/Dreamstime 36: Tarja Trygg

Lesson 3
38: Larry Landolfi/Science Source 40T: Thinkstock 40B: Thinkstock 42: Corbis Super RF/Alamy 46: NASA 47: NASA 48L: The Flowerpots or Hopewell Rocks, Bay of Fundy/Visuals Unlimited 48R: George Kroll/Dreamstime

Lesson 4
52: Fred Espenak/Science Source 54: Science Source 63: Thinkstock 64: NASA 65: iStockphoto 66: Wikimedia/NASA 67: NASA

Unit 2 Opener
68: NASA 69T: NASA/SDO 69C: Getty Images 69B: Wikimedia/NASA 71B: NASA Ames Research Center

Lesson 5
72: NASA/SDO 76: International Astronomical Union/NASA 77B: NASA/JPL-Caltech/Space Science Institute 78T: NASA/APL/SwRI 78C: NASA/JPL/JHUAPL 78B: NASA/ESA/Giotto Project 82: John Sanford/Science Source 84: Getty Images 85: Thinkstock 86: ASSOCIATED PRESS 87T: ASSOCIATED PRESS 87B: Wikimedia

Lesson 6
88: Getty Images 90T: Art Directors & TRIP/Alamy 90B: Thinkstock 91T: Design Pics Inc/Alamy 91C: Wikimedia/NASA 91B: NASA/JPL/Cornell University 94: NASA/Johns Hopkins University Applied Physics Laboratory/Carnegie Institution of Washington 95T: NASA 95B: NASA/Goddard Space Flight Center (GSFC) 96: JPL/California Institute of Technology/NASA 97: NASA 98: Wikimedia/NASA 99T: NASA/JPL-Caltech/MSSS 99B: Steve Lee (University of Colorado), Jim Bell (Cornell University), Mike Wolff (Space Science Institute), and NASA 102: NASA/JPL-Caltech/JAXA/ESA 103: Wikimedia/NASA 104: NASA/JPL-Caltech 105: Mars Science Laboratory (MSL)/NASA 106: NASA/JPL-Caltech/MSSS 107: NASA/JPL-Caltech/Malin Space Science Systems

Lesson 7
108: Wikimedia/NASA 110: NASA Ames Research Center 114: NASA/JPL/University of Arizona 115T: SPL/Science Source 115B: NASA/JPL/DLR 116: NASA/JPL/Space Science Institute 117: NASA/JPL-Caltech/SSI 118: Lawrence Sromovsky, University of Wisconsin-Madison/W.W. Keck Observatory 119: NASA/JPL 123: Dennis di Cicco/Corbis 125T: Wikimedia 126T: ASSOCIATED PRESS 126B: NASA 127: Comet Shoemaker-Levy 9 Approaching Jupiter in 1994 127: NASA, Hubble Space Telescope

Unit 3 Opener
128: NASA 129T: NASA, ESA, M. Robberto (Space Telescope Science Institute/ESA) and the Hubble Space Telescope Orion Treasury Project Team 129B: X-ray: NASA/CXC/SAO; Optical: Detlef Hartmann; Infrared: NASA/JPL-Caltech 131T: Thinkstock 131C: Science Source 131B: Wikimedia/NASA

Lesson 8
132: NASA, ESA, M. Robberto (Space Telescope Science Institute/ESA) and the Hubble Space Telescope Orion Treasury Project Team 135: Wikimedia/NASA 140: Wikimedia/NASA 141L: Wikimedia/NASA 141C: Wikimedia/NASA 141R: Walter Geiersperger/Corbis 141: Adeliepenguin/Dreamstime 142: iStockphoto 143: iStockphoto

Lesson 9
144: X-ray: NASA/CXC/SAO; Optical: Detlef Hartmann; Infrared: NASA/JPL-Caltech 148: Thinkstock 150T: ESA/Hubble & NASA 150C: Wikimedia/NASA 150B: NASA, ESA, and A. Aloisi (Space Telescope Science Institute and European Space Agency, Baltimore, Md.) 152: NASA; ESA; G. Illingworth, D. Magee, and P. Oesch, University of California, Santa Cruz; R. Bouwens, Leiden University; and the HUDF09 Team 154: SOTK2011/Alamy 155: ASSOCIATED PRESS 157: Shutterstock 158: NASA Ames/JPL-Caltech/T. Pyle 159: Science Source

Back Matter
160: Reto Stöckli, Nazmi El Saleous, and Marit Jentoft-Nilsen, NASA GSFC 162: Corbis Premium RF/Alamy 163: iStockphoto 164: Image Source Plus/Alamy 165: Thinkstock 167: Shutterstock 169: Shutterstock 170R: Shutterstock 171T: Karin Hildebrand Lau/Alamy 171B: A.J.D. Foto Ltd./Alamy 173: Thinkstock 177: Shutterstock 179: Shutterstock 181: Thinkstock 183: Shutterstock 185: Shutterstock 186T: Wikimedia 187T: Thinkstock 187C: Thinkstock 191T: Thinkstock 191C: Thinkstock 192B: iStockphoto 193T: Thinkstock 193C: Getty Images 193B: NASA 194: Thinkstock 195: Borislav Toskov/Dreamstime 196: Image Source Plus/Alamy 197: Hero Images Inc./Alamy 200: Blend Images/Alamy 201: iStockphoto 202L: Thinkstock 203: NASA/JPL 205: Thinkstock 208: Wikimedia 213: Ted Foxx/Alamy 214: iStockphoto